W9-BCY-980

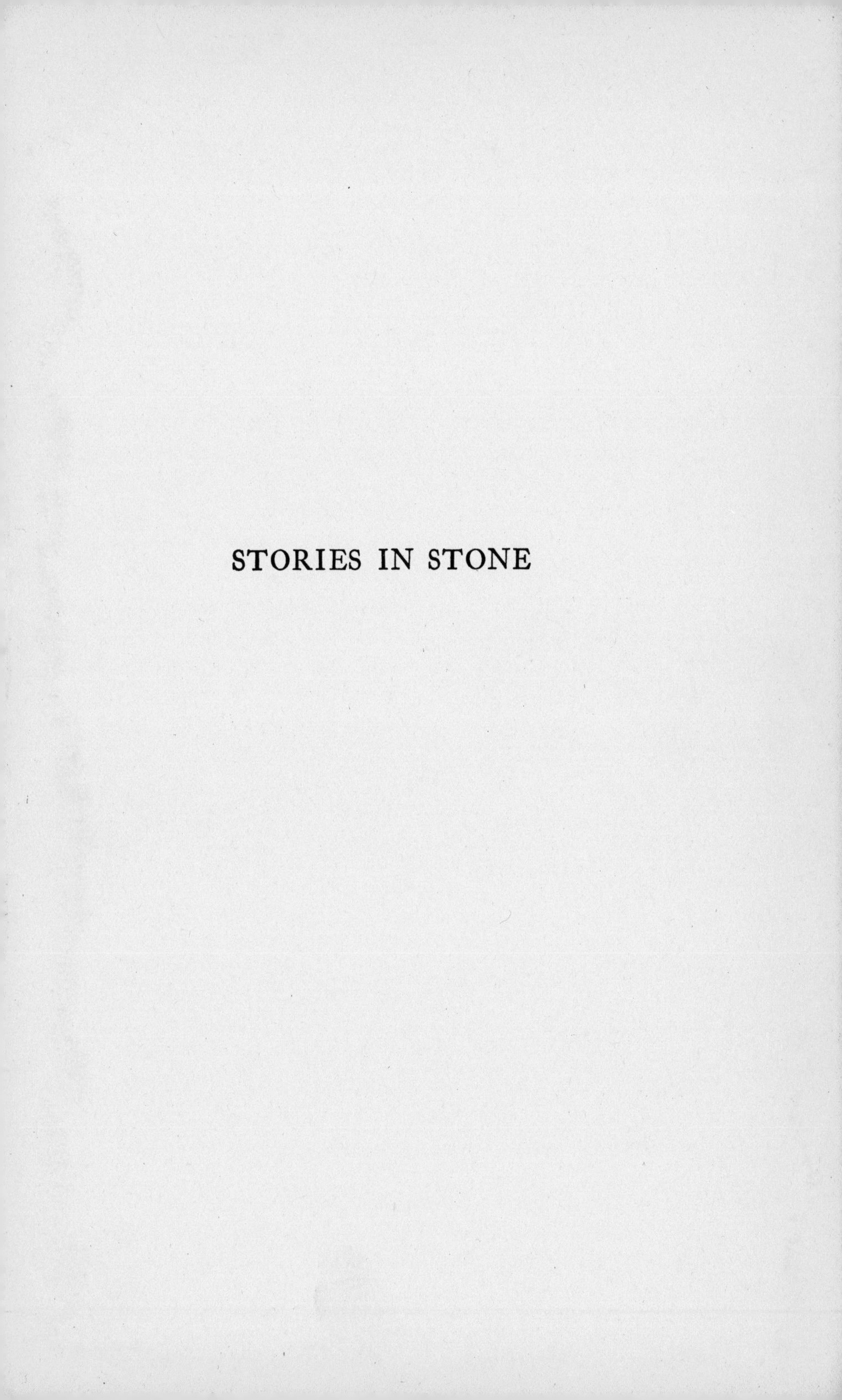

STORIES IN STONE

LIBRARY OF MODERN SCIENCES

A popular series treating their influence on the development of civilization

EDITORS

EDWIN E. SLOSSON, Ph.D., M. LUCKIESH, D.Sc., H. E. HOWE, M.S.

THE EARTH AND THE STARS, *By* C. G. ABBOT, *of the Smithsonian Institution.*

CHEMISTRY IN MODERN LIFE, *By* SVANTE ARRHENIUS, *Director of the Nobel Institute, translated by* CLIFFORD S. LEONARD, *Fellow, National Research Council: Department of Pharmacology, Yale University.*

ANIMALS OF LAND AND SEA, *By* AUSTIN CLARK, *Curator, Smithsonian Institution.*

CHEMISTRY IN THE WORLD'S WORK, *By* H. E. HOWE, *Editor, Industrial and Engineering Chemistry.*

STORIES IN STONE, *By* WILLIS T. LEE, *Late Geologist, United States Geological Survey, Washington, D. C.*

FOUNDATIONS OF THE UNIVERSE, *By* M. LUCKIESH, *Director, Lighting Research Laboratory, National Lamp Works of General Electric Company.*

THE MYSTERY OF MIND, *By* LEONARD TROLAND, *Professor of Psychology, Harvard University.*

SOIL AND CIVILIZATION, *By* MILTON WHITNEY, *Chief of the Bureau of Soils of the United States Department of Agriculture.*

THE HUMAN HABITAT, *By* ELLSWORTH HUNTINGTON, *Research Associate in Geography, Yale University.*

STORIES IN STONE

Telling of Some of the Wonderlands of Western America and Some of the Curious Incidents in the History of Geology

BY

WILLIS T. LEE

LATE GEOLOGIST, UNITED STATES GEOLOGICAL SURVEY
WASHINGTON, D. C.

AUTHOR OF "THE GEOLOGIC STORY OF THE ROCKY MOUNTAIN NATIONAL PARK," "THE FACE OF THE EARTH AS SEEN FROM THE AIR," "GUIDE BOOK OF THE WESTERN UNITED STATES," (IN PART), AND OTHER WORKS ON POPULAR, SCIENTIFIC AND ECONOMIC GEOLOGY

SEVENTH PRINTING

NEW YORK
D. VAN NOSTRAND COMPANY, INC.
250 FOURTH AVENUE

First Published November, 1926
Reprinted April 1927, May 1927
July 1928, August 1929, December 1932
February 1938

PRINTED IN THE UNITED STATES OF AMERICA

To Lovers of the Natural Beauty and the Grandeur of the Earth, to Those who Look to the Mountains for Pleasure, and to Those who Make the Rocks Yield their History and their Treasure of Knowledge, This Volume is Dedicated.

CONTENTS

ILLUSTRATIONS

INTRODUCTION

These stories in stone are offered with the hope that they may arouse in you the same enthusiastic interest that they arouse in me — that they may induce you to delve into the secrets of the earth and find abiding satisfaction.

There is romance in the rocks for him who can read their language. The fossils and the crystals, the pebbles and the sand, are the symbols in which the story of the earth is written. Some striking chapters of this great story are written in the scenic features of our own western country, in which are found most of the fine examples of natural expression here described and interpreted.

With the increase in the number of our national parks, the establishment of a National Park Service, and the organization of park associations, the intelligent appreciation of natural scenery, as well as the desire to know something about its meaning and its origin, is certain to increase.

Natural scenery is directly dependent on the character of the rocks. The kinds of plants that adorn a scene — the forests and the flowers — depend largely on the nature of the soil, and the nature of the soil depends on the composition of the rocks from which it is formed.

Great cliffs, picturesque waterfalls, and forested mountains do not simply happen. To find their underlying causes we search the records of past geologic ages. A full understanding and appreciation of a landscape necessitates a knowledge of the underlying rocks. It is hoped that this book may help to convey some of that knowledge.

The book is not offered as a text in geology. It is merely a collection of facts and tales which have proved fascinating to me and which I believe will prove interesting to you.

The work is not exhaustive. Volumes fail to exhaust such a subject. Geology is a young science and is growing day by day through new discoveries. The more clearly geology is understood the more clearly will the significance of the new discoveries appear.

To know truly the world we live in may well be one of our highest purposes, and even if the path of our knowledge shall be endless we shall find along it enough of wonder and of beauty to gladden us in our journey.

The Author

EDITOR'S NOTE

The author of this book, Dr. Willis T. Lee, died June 16, 1926, at the age of sixty-one, before the book was put in type. After several years of experience as a teacher of geology in colleges and universities, Doctor Lee entered the Government service as a member of the United States Geological Survey. In this capacity he made extended studies of the geologic formations of the West, particularly to determine their correlation — that is, their equivalence or succession in age — as a means of interpreting the geologic history of the earth. Throughout his work he displayed the initiative of the explorer and the critical observation and open mind of the man of science. He was the first Government scientist to use the airplane in geologic work. His exploration of the Carlsbad Cavern was another of his notable exploits. The diversity of his scientific interest is well shown in this book. In his death Science has lost a faithful servant.

G. M. W.

STORIES IN STONE

Chapter I

WHAT'S THE USE?

An Invitation

Would you like to know something of the earth on which we live and how it is made to yield us the means of life and happiness? And would it interest you to recall some of the curious concepts that have centered around the origin of the earth?

Would you like to *know* the *Grand Canyon*, or is it enough just to read about it? (Plate I) Are you satisfied to be introduced to *Niagara Falls* (Plate II), or would you like to be intimate with this world-famous cataract and feel its great pulsing life? Is it enough to be gently sprayed from a safe distance by a geyser or do you wish to descend in comprehensive imagination into the seething caldrons beneath the surface and know the forces that produce an Old Faithful? Are you satisfied to know in some vague, indefinite way that there is a volcanic mountain known as Vesuvius and that a pit of boiling lava exists at *Kilauea*, or do you long to know really what causes a volcanic eruption such as that which formed the crater of Taal? (Plate III)

If these things interest you, perhaps you will browse with me through the quaint volumes cited in the closing chapters of this book and scan some of those early conceptions which contained the germs of truth from which have sprung many of the beliefs of the present day.

The development of belief concerning the origin and general history of the earth is as interesting to some as the physical processes of the earth are to others. Perhaps some will join with me in an intense interest in the development of the science of the earth and follow the growth of knowledge from a time when "the earth was without form and void" in the minds of men, through the long periods of intellectual gloom when only an occasional flash of light penetrated the murky atmosphere of superstition and ignorance, to the present time, when facts are being placed in orderly arrangement and when natural law is finding its proper recognition.

Standards of Value

Let us consider first some of the tangible things that are near at hand and that affect the course of our life day by day, then some of those intangible things that are less obvious but no less real. These things cannot be sharply separated any more than work and play can be sharply separated in real life. Both are necessary.

There is an ideal standard by which values may be judged, as well as a practical standard. A thing may be useful for increasing our material comfort, or it may be employed for broadening human knowledge and for touching the finer emotions. The science of geology stands the test of judgment by both standards. The mind as well as the body must be fed. The coal mine furnishes the means of bodily comfort; the oil field, the means of travel; and natural scenery, an important means of enjoyment.

The ability to interpret natural scenery properly depends on a knowledge of the forces which produced it. We may admire the beauty of a landscape or marvel at its grandeur, but we must know how it was formed before we can appreciate its full significance. A great canyon appears wonderful as we gaze into its depths; but it appears far more wonderful when we know how it came into being. A volcanic explosion like that of Katmai seems astounding. But astonishment does not satisfy the inquiring mind. To fathom such mysteries, men are willing to spend time and treasure and even to risk life.

From the earth we draw those material things which are necessary for life and happiness. The science of the earth is fundamental, for it treats of those things. This science guides us in the search for mineral wealth and aids us in understanding the forces which produced this wealth. A study of geologic processes leads to an understanding of the laws which contribute to our daily happiness, for these processes have been in operation from the beginning, shaping the earth into a pleasant place for human habitation. Thus practical considerations are not far separated from the theoretical. Applied geology and pure geology join hands.

Discoveries and Applications

It is quite impossible to foresee what applications may be made of a new discovery or how an understanding of a natural law may be applied. In the early stages of civilization discoveries were accidental. Primitive man probably learned by accident how to use a rude flint implement, and the Stone Age followed. Later, men discovered in some way that bronze tools were better than flint. The use of iron and copper and aluminum followed, and we are now learning to use materials that still seem somewhat mysterious, such as helium and tungsten and radium.

But learning new things is a slow process. The struggle out of the slough of ignorance is difficult and discouraging. The school of "hard knocks" has more graduates than any other.

Many have tried short cuts. Some there are who still believe it is possible to find the treasures of earth through the guidance of dreams and of charms. And many have faith in appliances which pass under the general name of "doodlebugs."

Principles and "Doodlebugs"

The hope of progress lies in understanding, and an ever-increasing number of young people are going out to face Nature equipped with a knowledge of Nature's laws. In geology, as in every other field of activity, knowledge is power. It was a geologist who developed the fundamental principle that oil is found chiefly in anticlines and domes. The recognition of this principle has helped to increase the production of petroleum from a few barrels a day seventy years ago to nearly 3,000,000 barrels a day at the present time.

But a trained mind is necessary for taking advantage of even well established laws. The element of chance sometimes enters to confound the wise. The trained man assures us that the "water witch" cannot "smell" water any farther than can the man without a forked stick. Yet water is found in many a well that has been located by someone who used a hazel twig. The fact that underground water is present almost everywhere and that it would have been found with the same amount of effort in almost any other place does not seem particularly impressive compared with the fact that water was found where the hazel twig pointed.

Many oil wells and many bodies of ore have been located by the use of "doodlebugs." Most such wells are dry and most of the ore bodies located in this way are worthless, but occasionally a strike is made and is referred to as proof that the method is correct. The numberless failures are forgotten.

Some years ago a prospector in the Rocky Mountains learned that rich ore is to be expected where two veins cross.

In his search for wealth he found a place where a tree had fallen across the prostrate trunk of another tree. He remembered that something "crossed" denotes rich ore but he had forgotten what it was that should be crossed. He dug his prospecting shaft where the tree trunks crossed and found ore. It so happened that a shaft anywhere near this point would have entered the body of ore which he found. But it was quite useless to tell him this. He had proved to his own satisfaction that something crossed denotes rich ore.

Pure Science Better than Pure Nonsense

Examples of this misapplication of correct principles might be multiplied indefinitely, but they serve no more useful purpose than to give warnings of what not to do. Much more useful are examples of a correct principle followed to a useful conclusion.

Underlying the art of geology is the so-called pure science, from which spring all the rules and guiding principles for practical geologic work, and many a line of research pursued in the cause of science with little thought of practical application has yielded information of great material benefit. Witness a certain study in glacial geology:—

Dr. W. C. Alden, of the United States Geological Survey, worked for years mapping with painstaking accuracy numerous glacial deposits and studying the behavior of the sheet of ice which overwhelmed Wisconsin in the Great Ice Age.

" Such a study is all very well for those who are interested in the story of the earth. But what's the use? It has no practical application." So argued the uninitiated.

When the study of the glacial deposits was undertaken, the present great network of automobile roads had scarcely been started. But soon after Doctor Alden's report was published engineers in Wisconsin needed gravel for building roads.

The glacial gravels were found to be suitable, and Doctor Alden's map proved to be a valuable guide in finding them. Considered only as a means of finding road metal this map is said to have been worth many times the entire cost of Doctor Alden's investigation.

Pure geology may be fitly applied to the interpretation of natural scenery, for the surface of the earth — the landscapes and the natural features that excite our wonder and delight — are all the results of geologic processes.

Geology and Scenery

Some of the choicest bits of natural scenery in the world are found in the wonderlands of America. Many of the best of these natural wonders have been reserved for the enjoyment of the public in national parks and national monuments, where they may remain forever unchanged in the form that Nature gave them. Each park contains a notable example of some special type of scenery. In Kilauea (Pls. V and VI) we may see the results of an active volcano; in Lassen Volcanic Park (Pl. VII) we may see a mountain that was built up by volcanic eruption; in Yellowstone Park we may examine the results of dying volcanic activity; in Zion Canyon we may see a most remarkable example of a stream-cut gorge; and in the Grand Canyon we may behold the most sublime chasm in the world.

The national parks and monuments and many other tracts of land that might appropriately be reserved as parks are full of attractive scenes that are worthy of close study. Each park illustrates a special type of landscape, and each possesses scientific as well as scenic interest. These parks contain many of the natural wonders of the world.

Before much of the earth's surface was known to cultured people there were seven wonders of the world; now there are "seventy times seven."

I Want to Know!

But to the intelligent mind it is not enough that wonders are made visible. Such a mind is always reaching out after causes. "How did it happen?" is often the first question asked. "I want to know" is an exclamation so familiar that its real significance may be lost.

Probably no sentence in any language is more familiar than that accounting for the origin of the universe: "In the beginning God created the heavens and the earth." After the exclamations of wonder commonly heard as a party of sight-seers approaches a great cliff or enters a deep canyon, the first question usually is, — what made it?

Some may care little for the processes by which results are obtained. They are content to contemplate the finished product. But the genuinely appreciative observer is not satisfied with visible objects alone. With mental insight he goes back of the object to its primary cause. Back of a painting an artist sees the years of training that made the painter.

Few of us are content merely to see a cathedral. While we are enjoying its beauty we wish to know its origin and its history. We seek to know how and when the architect worked his dreams into stone.

Ruins — especially prehistoric ruins — become more interesting as the cloudy mystery of the past clears away. By whom were they made? What is their story?

In like manner the architecture of nature is fascinating in proportion to the measure of appreciative understanding with which it is viewed. To him who knows geology the earth is not a mass of dead rock; it is a living, pulsing body, ever changing by movements so deliberate and majestic that only by mental insight can we behold them. To him who knows, the mountain is not a forbidding pile of rocks; it is the visible embodiment of a fascinating story in the life of the earth. To him who has mental vision, the canyon is not a finished creation existent from the beginning; it represents only one stage in the process by which highlands are gradually torn down and swept into the sea: its story is still being told.

To understand and appreciate the natural scenery of the wonderlands of western America we must know at least the elements of geology, just as we must know conditions and methods of mineral deposition in order to prospect intelligently for the deposits of ore.

To this end, it seems appropriate to call attention, as is done in the closing chapters of this book, to some of the conspicuous incidents in the development of belief concerning the nature of the earth and to apply the ideas thus developed to the interpretation of scenery. I hasten, however, to assure you now that I have no intention of going exhaustively into the tiresome details of a dead past. Rather would I merely glance over its cloudy vistas and as quickly as possible note a few of the most conspicuous milestones in the course of events by which we have arrived at the present understanding of the earth and of the natural processes which brought it into being and adorned it with noble mountains, gorgeously colored canyons, and broad, verdure-covered plains.

Aids to Understanding

And so, renewing the invitation, I bid you come with me if you wish to see the wonders of the earth; to know its story; to have some understanding of the great drama of creation, and learn to read the language of the rocks. Having learned this language, you may live in retrospective imagination through the geologic ages. But bring with you every means at your disposal that will aid your understanding.

Bring your knowledge of physics and chemistry, in order to

Plate I. North Side of Grand Canyon as Seen from Grand Canyon Station.

G, Granite and gneiss; U, Sandstone, red shale and limestone (Unkar); T, Sandstone (Tonto) forming the bench called the Tonto Platform; Sh, Shale of Tonto group, lying directly on quartzite of Unkar; R, Limestone (Redwall); S, Red sandstone and shale (Supai); C, Gray sandstone (Coconino); K, Limestone (Kaibab). The Redwall butte in the center is Cheops Pyramid; beyond are Buddha and Manu temples. Background is Kaibab Plateau.

Plate II. Niagara Falls as Seen from an Airplane, Looking Northeastward (Downstream).

The rough surface at the bottom of the photograph represents the rapids above the V of the Horseshoe Falls. In the upper right hand corner is the power plant. Official photograph U. S. Army Air Service.

understand how the oceans were formed and how the mountains were raised. The wisest physicists have tried and are still trying their skill on the great earth problems.

Bring your logic and give all your powers of reason full scope. You will need them all.

Bring your knowledge of zoölogy and of botany and in its light trace the path of progress by which living organisms found their way from lower to higher forms, the offspring ever improving on the parent stock.

Bring all your skill in literary expression and exercise it in describing the beauty and grandeur of the earth.

Bring imagination, by means of whose telescopic powers you may explore regions where knowledge has not yet entered.

An Elixir of Life

From the days of Ponce de Leon and his search for the spring of perpetual youth to the present time, men have desired long life. Let me prescribe an elixir by which you may live a million years.

Search out an understanding of the earth with all the helps just mentioned and by their aid live through the misty ages so long gone that reason staggers in evaluating their duration. Although you cannot number the uncounted periods of time or measure the unmeasured ages through which the earth has passed, you can, in imagination, live through some of those ages and enjoy the kaleidoscopic changes by which the planet on which you live has reached its present state of perfection.

In imagination you may witness the collision of stars in their uncharted course and see, as it were, the dust of their impact scattered in the heavens. You may see the star dust gather into worlds and the worlds organize themselves into systems. From seeming chaos you may see the great blazing sun travel from some unknown region of boundless space toward some other unknown region, accompanied by his orderly, obedient followers, the planets.

You may, in imagination, see the earth grow from an inconspicuous globe scarcely larger than its numerous neighbors to a masterful body which has gathered to itself most of these neighbors and incorporated them into a compact symmetrical mass. In this welding of parts, who may say what wars of the elements were waged? But out of the conflict of forces came order and symmetry of form. And out of the hidden laboratories within the earth came the oceans of water and the protecting cloak of the atmosphere without which no living form could exist.

Following still the path of imagination, behold the rise of living beings from simple, minute unicellular forms developing slowly, on the one hand, into plants, and on the other, into animals. Follow these in imagination from age to age and note how each period was characterized by its own peculiar forms of plants and animals, each group adapting itself to the physical conditions of its own time.

The Earth's Activities

There was an age when the furnaces of Vulcan belched fire from many a vent and poured out molten rock in great seething floods. An age followed during which these tumultuous floods of lava, now cold and hard, were covered with water and myriads of sea animals contributed their shells as records of conditions ever changing with the march of time.

At times the climate was warm, and tropical plants grew almost from pole to pole. At other times, the same regions were covered with great sheets of ice, which slowly but irresistibly moved over the surface from the cold poles to the warmer zones, smoothing the country and grinding the surface rocks to powder.

Following still further the path of imagination, behold the forests of bygone days collecting carbon and storing it in the swamps for preservation in beds of coal.

With mental vision, see the minute plants and animals on the land and in the sea gathering the carbon and the hydrogen and each, in its tiny laboratory, molding hydrocarbons of infinite variety destined to be gathered in great rock reservoirs in the form of oil and gas.

In brief, if you properly use the geologic elixir of life, you may see in imagination those processes, operating throughout the ages, by which the earth was stored with ten thousand useful substances and decorated with unnumbered charms.

Chapter II

THE IDEAL AND THE PRACTICAL

One of the objects of this book is to put on record some of the tales that seem worth perpetuating, and certain incidents that seem worthy of serious consideration. This chapter does not exhaust the stock. It merely suggests lines of thought that have interested me and that I hope may interest you.

It has been said that scientific men have a message for the world but do not know how to tell it. In a measure this may be true, for the study of natural science is relatively new and its followers have been so intent on discovering its fascinating mysteries that they have paid little attention to the manner of describing them. However, the mode of expression is of secondary importance. The facts count for more than the language, just as a painting is more important than the frame in which it is exhibited.

A Message

The message which I am trying to present seems to be so interesting that the manner of presentation should matter little. The rhetorician who is looking for literary perfection may look elsewhere. I am concerned chiefly in presenting to those who are eager to know of them the things which fascinate me. For this reason I am writing chiefly for the young men and the young women who read as they run, and for the boys and girls of today who are to be the seers of tomorrow, and for the lovers of God's great outdoors who want fact rather than fiction. I am writing for those people who are young in heart although their hair may be as white as mine, and for those who, like myself, find facts stranger than fiction and more exciting than the machinations of fancy.

I am trying to do for some one else what a good friend did for me years ago — a friend whose hair is now a crown of glory on his kindly brow. Let me digress a moment.

Inspiration

Years ago in the little Pennsylvania town where the first years of my life were spent, entertainments were rare, movies had not been invented, and good stereopticon pictures were unknown to me. But one boy from that town had chosen to be a teacher of geology. He had obtained what we then called a magic lantern, a crude apparatus for projecting pictures onto a screen by means of light from a kerosene lamp. The lantern would be laughed at today, and the slides — what crudities they were! But to me they were wonderful!

Each vacation when the geologist came home the magic lantern came with him and the pictures were exhibited. I counted the months, the weeks, and the days from vacation to vacation, and the hours of the day until finally I sat in open-eyed wonder gazing at those imperfect representations of extinct animals and ancient landscapes. My imagination was stirred profoundly and there settled upon me, never to depart, a determination to know something of the wonders of this old earth of ours.

If through the imperfections of this book, which may be as obvious to some readers as those of the magic lantern pictures are to me now, I can pass this enthusiastic determination on to some one else, I shall not have written in vain.

There are two general classes of readers that I hope to reach: those who would turn a knowledge of geology to practical uses, such as the teacher and the mining engineer, and those who, though busy most of the time with other things, turn to the mountains and the canyons for their recreation. It is of these travelers that I am now thinking chiefly, for in this commercial age there is need for idealism. All work and no play sends men to the madhouse.

Idealism and Commercialism

The idealists are numerous — those who would like to know the secrets of nature but who have been denied the opportunity of learning them. The intense interest in natural scenery is eloquently revealed by the crowds that flock to the national and municipal parks. Many of the public playgrounds are not yet equipped for entertaining guests or even for recording the number of visitors; yet the available records show that in the year 1925 between two and three million people took enough interest in the natural features preserved in the parks to spend much time and money to see them.

But while idealism should be fostered, commercialism should not be discouraged. Both are necessary, for both body and mind must be fed. Long ago it was said of certain things which some thought were more important than other things, "these things ye ought to have done and not to have left the other undone." There are many practical reasons why the laws of nature should be understood. Let me illustrate.

The Man Who Knows

A few years ago a man who had worked hard and long to keep his family comfortable in a modest home tried to dissuade his son from "wasting time and money" going to college. He objected especially to the study of what he termed "useless things," such as geology. But the young man was not dissuaded. He had observed that boys who *know* find better opportunities than those who do not know. He liked college and he liked the study of geology. He continued to follow his own judgment in the face of parental opposition.

A few years later this boy was placed in charge of one of the field parties of the United States Geological Survey and sent out to gather information on the natural resources of the country. A part of his duty was to employ other men and to direct their activities. Among those employed by him was his father, who was given a position as teamster. The older man knew no geology, but he could take care of horses and could make himself generally useful about camp. If he remembered his former opposition to his son's ambition he said nothing of it. The son remembered — but he also said nothing. A few years later the young man was put in charge of the field operations of a large oil company, and in due time he developed a business of his own.

The older man was like many others who are too shortsighted to see the great opportunities open to those who are prepared. But fortunately there are many who, like this younger man, are far-sighted enough to see that there are possibilities in the future and to prepare for them.

Why Worry?

The question is heard on every hand, "What's the use of learning things that will never be needed?" What boy has not been scolded for dreaming when he should have been at work? What girl, for building air castles and missing her lesson? There is no help for it. The scolding must be endured. The parent has forgotten his daydreams, and the teachers' air castles have fallen. But who shall say what has been the lifelong influence of some childish vision?

Demand for Geologists

Never in the history of the world has there been greater demand than now for men in the natural sciences. This is true particularly in geology. Never before has there been so insistent a demand for the products ot the earth — products that are being used in immense quantities. More coal is needed; it is difficult to get enough iron to supply the demand; there is always a ready market for gold and silver; and the cry for gasoline and other products of petroleum is becoming more and more feverishly insistent. Hundreds of other products of the rocks find ready market. There is a constant demand for the services of those who know where to find the minerals and how to extract them from the rocks. There is unending search for potash and there is fear that the supply of platinum will fail. Nitrates are so scarce and so much in demand that efforts are being made to supply them by artificial means.

The call for increased production of food is world-wide. Food is the product of the soil, and soil is produced from the rocks. In a very real sense the production of food is a geologic problem. The character of the soil varies with the kind of rock from which it is produced. The soil of a limestone region is quite different from that of a sandstone region. Each is adapted to certain kinds of crops and not to others.

A knowledge of the science of the earth is useful in many occupations. The engineer must know the strength of his foundation and the builder the resistance of his material. Heavy buildings, bridge piers and dams must rest on foundations firm enough for their support. Sometimes the most rudimentary knowledge of geology would save an engineer years of labor and the useless expenditure of millions of dollars.

Plate III. Crater of Taal Volcano, Philippine Islands, as Seen from an Airplane.
Official photograph U. S. Army Air Service.

PLATE IV. EASTERN FACE OF THE GRAND TETON, IN WESTERN WYOMING, AS SEEN FROM AN AIRPLANE.

The lower slopes are covered sparsely with tall pine trees. The middle slopes are dotted with ice fields and with talus slopes that mark great accumulations of slide rock. The high peaks rise steeply into the clouds. Official photograph U. S. Army Air Service.

Practical Applications

Recently an important viaduct was planned to carry a railroad across a valley. The plans called for a pier near the center of the valley. The nature of its foundation was not properly determined until work on other parts of the viaduct was far advanced. Apparently the engineers in charge did not realize — perhaps did not know — that this valley lies in a region where the glaciers of the Great Ice Age had filled preëxisting valleys with sand, clay, and boulders.

As the work of construction progressed it became evident that the center pier had been located in the course of an old channel that had been filled with clay and quicksand. For a time it seemed doubtful whether a good base could be found for the central pier, and other parts of the viaduct were finished long before an adequate foundation for the central pier was reached. A little geologic knowledge and enough forethought to determine the underground conditions before plans were finished might have saved much trouble and prevented much waste of time and money.

Several years ago a dam was built across the Pecos River, in New Mexico, to store water for irrigation. The bed of the reservoir consisted in part of gypsum. A slight knowledge of geology should have warned the promoters that a reservoir on beds of gypsum was about as suitable for storing water as a cup made of sugar would be for serving tea. The water soon found underground passages, which were rapidly enlarged, for the water took into solution the gypsum through which it flowed. At the time of my visit these underground passages were carrying the entire flow of the river and the reservoir was empty.

Some attributed the failure of this reservoir to the inexperience of those who had charge of it and argued that it might have been saved by skilled engineers. Settlers were depending on the reservoir for the irrigation of their crops. The United States Reclamation Service tried to save the community from ruin and set for its experienced engineers the herculean task of outwitting nature.

Hercules had succeeded in deflecting a river from its natural course; so also did the engineers. But although a new reservoir site was chosen and a dam built to control the water of the river, the water refused to be held in control. Hercules himself would not have been able to hold water in a gypsum basin. After years of fruitless effort no way has been found to stop all the leaks, and the large storage reservoirs here are rated as failures.

One more example may be cited to illustrate the need of understanding the nature of the rocks where dams are to be constructed.

The Zuni Indians needed a storage reservoir for irrigation, and a site was selected on the Zuni River in western New Mexico, where lava from a volcano, now extinct, had flowed across the old valley. After this lava had cooled and hardened the river had cut a narrow channel through it. Here the engineers constructed a dam, but before the reservoir was filled the water found a way of escape through the rocks at one side of the dam.

When the molten lava had spread over the country in past ages it had buried the soil and loose sand of the old surface in the bottom of the valley. As the water rose behind the dam the pressure finally became great enough to force water through the unconsolidated material under the lava, and much of the fine material was washed out, allowing the undermined lava to break and settle in a fractured mass, through which the water easily made its way.

Theory and Practice

The benefits of a knowledge of geology in mining are so obvious that they should require no discussion; and yet invidious distinctions are frequently made between "practical knowledge" and "theoretical guesses," or, as some express it, "theoretical nonsense." Theory and practice are equally useful and are dependent on each other. Practical results frequently follow the application of theories of some one who has thought out possibilities.

Prophetic Geology

The science of geology attains one of its highest objectives when it presents a deduction that points the way to obtain practical results. An illustration of such a deduction was given in connection with the proposed disposal of chemical waste from one of the Government plants started at Sheffield, Ala., for the fixation of atmospheric nitrogen. This plant is so situated that surface drainage from it would be difficult and expensive, and, furthermore, there seemed to be danger that the discharge of chemical waste into the neighboring streams would produce bad results. The problem was incidentally submitted to a geologist, who ascertained that the plant rests on limestone, a kind of rock that is likely to be honeycombed by caves. He advised trying underground drainage by means of drill holes. The plan proposed met with the usual opposition from so-called "practical men," who made the customary disparaging remarks about "scientific theories," but a trial hole was started close to a small lake near the plant, and when the drill reached a depth of 175 feet and a trench had been dug from the lake to the hole the lake water quickly disappeared through some subterranean passage.

Science and Utility

An example of the commercial application of a theory came to light some years ago. A coal mine in New Mexico was abandoned when the coal bed seemed to have been lost through faulting. The rocks had been disturbed by some earth movement, and it was supposed that where the coal disappeared the bed had been faulted out of place and eroded away. On this supposition the mine was abandoned, the camp was deserted, and the railroad connections were removed.

A geologist visited the deserted mine and found in the rocks the fossil tooth of an extinct mammal. By means of this tooth the geologic age of the rocks was determined. The geologist was then able to assure the officials of the coal company that their coal bed had not been eroded away. On this assurance a drill was put in operation, the lost bed was located, and the railroad was rebuilt. A new mine was opened and has been in operation ever since.

Nevertheless memory is short and men here, as in many other regions, with supercilious smile ask the geologist "What's the use of wasting time looking for curious rocks; what good are they; can't you find something useful to do?"

If we think for a moment of the quantities of mineral matter used we will not wonder at the increasing demand for men who understand geology. Nearly a billion and a half tons of coal were mined in 1925. Men are wanted who understand coal.

Half a century ago petroleum occupied so humble a place in the industrial world that it attracted little attention. At present the world is using oil at the rate of more than a billion barrels a year; and we take pride in the fact that two thirds of this amount is produced in the United States. The rapid expansion of the oil industry and the ever-increasing use of petro-

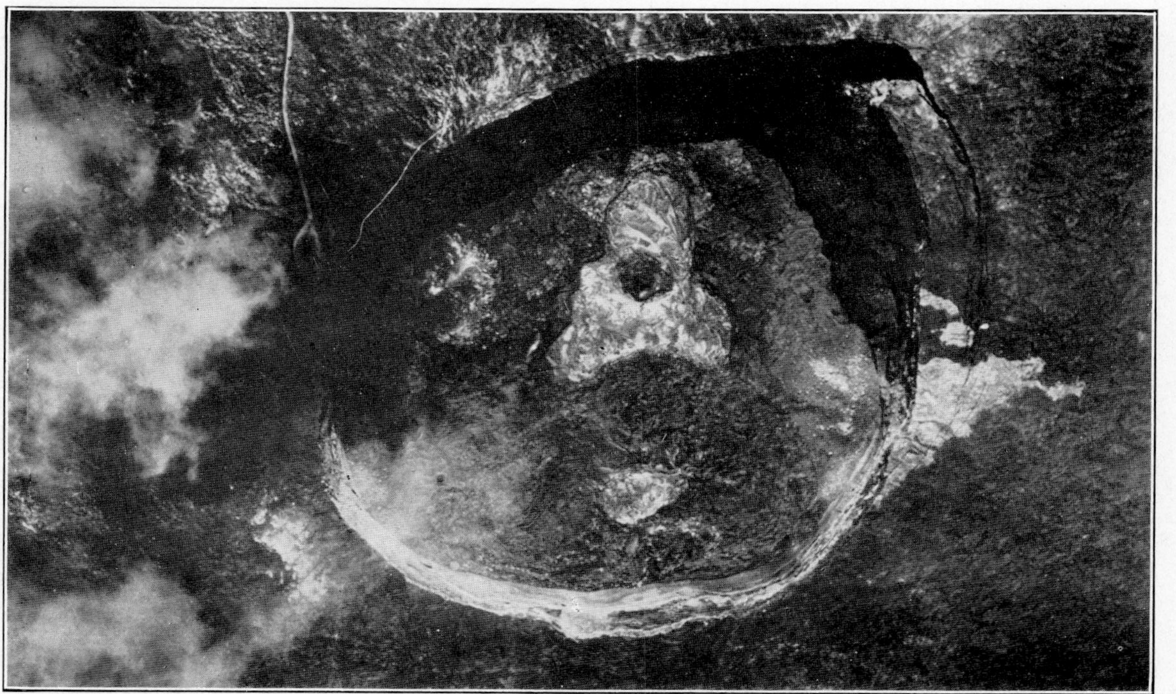

Plate V. The Great Fire Pit of Kilauea Seen from an Airplane at a Height of 4,000 feet, November 9, 1923.

This opening, about 3,500 feet across, is the vent or chimney of the volcanic furnace under the mountain. It may be considered the safety valve through which escape the gases that, if confined too long, might blow off the top of the mountain. Such an explosion did occur May 22, 1924, during which the pit was greatly enlarged. (See Pl. VI.) Official photograph U. S. Army Air Service.

Plate VI. A Volcanic Eruption of the Explosive Type.

The dust cloud of Kilauea, 11,500 feet high, shot out of the fire pit (see Pl. V) May 22, 1924, at a velocity of 780 feet a minute. The photograph was taken from the observatory, 2.1 miles from the fire pit. The indistinct parts denote clouds beginning to form as the hot vapor condenses. This explosion was a great surprise to those who were accustomed to regard Kilauea as a quiet and well-behaved volcano. Photograph by H. T. Stearns.

leum has created a demand for geologists who are able to see in the rocks the signs that point to oil. In petroleum regions the geologist is king. No one there asks, "What's the use?"

Fossils and Oil

A few years ago a geologist busied himself in California collecting fossil shells, studying them, and giving them long names which no one else seemed to be interested in. Some inquired what could be more useless from a practical point of view than studying the remains of animals that had perished long ages ago? What possible interest could the business world, which paid the bills, have in these remains of extinct animals? What difference did it make whether the geologist gave a shell some unpronounceable name or tossed it aside as a useless curiosity? So argued those who did not know.

The geologist discovered in the course of his study that certain kinds of shells are found in rocks that contain petroleum. By close observation of the fossils he was able to determine where oil was most likely to be found, and by a knowledge of the structure of the rocks he was able to tell the drillers how deep they must go in order to penetrate the oil-bearing stratum.

Since that time this geologist has been connected with the production of oil, and by means of his knowledge of fossil shells he has been able to add more value in dollars and cents to the wealth of the country than the study of fossils has cost since the science of paleontology began.

Franklin's Reply

The question asked so often, "What's the use" of this or that investigation, was properly answered by Benjamin Franklin, who replied to a similar question, "What's the use of a newborn babe?"

It is often as difficult to explain the use of certain work as it is to foretell what a child may accomplish in life. The geologist has special difficulty in certain parts of the country in meeting insistent demands to know just why opportunity should be given for an examination of private property and why he should receive certain information that seems not to concern him. Inability to explain why an item of information may be useful is no proof that it is useless.

Many a man now recognized as a benefactor of his race was once regarded as an impracticable dreamer.

Illustrations

The story goes that a few years ago Professor Langley, then Secretary of the Smithsonian Institution in Washington, was trying to persuade Congress to appropriate money for experiments on flying-machines. "Useless waste of money" many said. "Crazy mortal!" said others. "A loon isn't to be compared with a man who thinks he can fly like a bird!" But one man wiser than the others said, "Let him alone. Some day he may stumble upon something worth while." Unfortunately the sensitive heart of the great scientist broke under the derisive laughter of the nearsighted public, but the man who tried to help him lives to watch exploits of air men such as were never dreamed of in Langley's day. He lives to see the world stand in awe before the accomplishments of aëronautics and to see men excel Columbus in daring flight around the world.

Let the dreamer alone! Some kinds of dreams come true.

Many stories are told of trivial circumstances that have led to important results. Everyone is familiar with the statement that the cackling of geese saved Rome. Many a great discovery has been made because of some little circumstance that hundreds have passed without notice.

From a tale familiar to mining men we learn that in 1902 Ben Paddock, riding over a rocky trail in western Arizona, noticed some gleaming particles in one of the rocks. Others had traveled the same way but had not seen the particles. They interested Ben, although he did not know what they were. He gathered as much of the rock as his horse could carry and took it to Camp Mohave, where he sold it for $500.00. Later the Vivian gold mine was opened where this ore was found.

Many a man walked over the placer grounds of California before their value became known. The gold-bearing rocks of Cripple Creek in Colorado were prospected for years before some one of keen observation found the ore.

Untold generations of ignorant savages roamed over the diamond fields of South Africa without knowing the value of the treasure beneath their feet. Many a white child played with the pretty pebbles before anyone knew what they were, until Doctor Atherstone recognized then as diamonds.

Some years ago a road was built through the Phœnix Mountains in Arizona. Many a traveler passed over the road, perhaps dozing across the weary miles or regretting the opportunities he had missed, so blinded with self-pity that he could not see opportunities at his feet. But one man of sharp eyesight and keen insight noticed some red substance in one of the rocks at the side of the road. He wondered what it was. Probably others had wondered. But here is the difference: this man took a piece of the rock and had it examined. The red material proved to be cinnabar, the mineral from which mercury or quicksilver is obtained. A mercury mine was opened where he found the ore.

It pays to be wide awake even in the dreamy desert.

Sometimes the element of chance interferes with our plans. Some curse their luck and others turn the chance to advantage. We are all familiar with the statement that had not Bunyan been imprisoned he would never have written Pilgrim's Progress. It is not pleasant to be imprisoned. But if we are, we may still continue to make *progress* in one way or another.

Misfortune led to the discovery of gold at Gold Road, in Arizona, in 1902. The story runs that Joe Jeneres, a Mexican prospector, had the misfortune to lose his burros. Forage was scarce and the animals strayed into the hills in search of food. In the desert the loss of animals is serious. Joe went in search of them. He found not only the burros but also the gold ore he was looking for. Soon thereafter the Gold Road mine was opened where the animals had strayed.

But while we are considering the geological application of the principle that "Great oaks from little acorns grow" we may do well to consider also that some little things start great growths of foolishness.

In a prospective oil field that I once examined, some one had found a number of small rock concretions commonly known as ironstones. They had nothing to do with oil. But some wag had solemnly informed the finder that they were *oil beans*. Thereafter the supposed oil beans were collected in great number as proof that oil was present over a wide area. No oil has yet been found there.

PLATE VII. LASSEN PEAK, IN LASSEN VOLCANIC NATIONAL PARK, CALIFORNIA, THE ONLY ACTIVE VOLCANO IN THE UNITED STATES PROPER.

It is 10,465 feet high and was built up by lava extruded during a long series of eruptions. It stands in a region characterized by volcanic vents, hot springs, mud geysers, and other features resulting from igneous activity.

PLATE VIII. MOUNT MCKINLEY, THE HIGHEST MOUNTAIN IN AMERICA (ALTITUDE 20,300 FEET), AS SEEN FROM THE NORTHWEST AT A DISTANCE OF 15 MILES.

Photograph by A. H. Brooks.

Chapter III

LANDSCAPES, NEW AND OLD, IN THE GRAND CANYON NATIONAL PARK

Ever since the days when my youthful imagination was fired by pictures of the extinct animals and ancient landscapes referred to in the preceding chapter, I have been interested in these old animals and landscapes. To this interest I added that which I found in modern landscapes when, in the course of my work as a geologist of the United States Geological Survey, I had opportunity to see many of those American landscapes which in all parts of the world are regarded with wonder and admiration.

A Personally Conducted Tour

In the first chapter of this book an invitation was extended to consider with me some of the great natural scenic wonders of America. Our personally conducted tour of modern landscapes and of scenes of long ago, reconstructed in imagination from the rocks, will start at America's greatest scene, the Grand Canyon of Colorado River. Here, as at other places to be visited, we shall first scan the landscape beneath our eyes and then proceed to reconstruct for mental vision the landscapes of bygone ages.

The Grand Canyon is selected as our point of departure because it exhibits the rocks of the earliest geologic periods. Other parks will be visited in such order that the geologic periods will be considered in order from oldest to youngest.

The geologic record consists mainly of sedimentary beds — that is, beds deposited in water (Plate XIV). If a place could be found where sediments had been deposited continuously from the beginning of deposition to the present day and the beds thus formed were cut vertically so that their edges could be viewed from the side, the cut would show an unbroken geologic column. This column might be subdivided and its parts named and described so as to form a table of geologic time. But over large areas periods of uplift and erosion intervened between periods of deposition. Every such interruption in deposition produces what geologists term an unconformity. At many places the time divisions shown in the complete geologic column may be absent in whole or in part and be represented by lines of unconformity.

Each geologic age had its peculiar and characteristic forms of animal and plant life. As time progressed, the surface of the earth was changed. Through inconceivably long periods highlands were worn down and lowlands were built up, rivers changed their course, swamps were formed where dry land had been, lands were subdivided, and seas changed their places.

As the changes progressed, plants and animals were obliged to change their habits or perish. This necessity of adaptation to new conditions gave to each age its characteristic forms of life. Many of these forms are preserved as fossils, and from them something of the life of each age is known.

The length of the geologic ages can only be estimated. No reliable measure of time in years can be given. Many estimates have been made by men who have given the subject special attention and therefore are best qualified to judge. But the estimates should not be taken too precisely. At best they are only relative approximations to the truth.

The plateaus of central-western America, in which the Grand Canyon is cut, extend from Wyoming southwestward into Arizona and from central Colorado westward into Utah. This region is one of rugged mountains and tablelands that rise from one to two miles above the sea, and the canyons are cut deep into a varied assortment of gorgeously colored rocks. These rocks are carved by rain and stream (Pl. XV), frost and wind, into countless forms, which for variety of charm and beauty of color challenge the attention of the world.

Variety of Scenes

The variety of scenes is still further increased by volcanic activity, both ancient and recent. At some places quantities of molten matter were poured out. This molten matter hardened into resistant rock and protected the softer rocks beneath it, which elsewhere were worn away. Hence in some places the high plateaus are covered with hard volcanic rock. In other places the older rocks were broken and molten rock was forced into the cracks of the fractured mass. In still other places streams of molten rock poured into the canyons and interfered with the normal flow of the streams.

Since 1869, when Major Powell and his intrepid companions made their daring exploration of the Colorado River, travelers, with one accord, have given the Grand Canyon an exalted place among the wonders of the world.

This chasm, a mile deep and ten miles or more wide, presents the reciprocal of the ordinary mountain landscape. It is the mountain upside down, or outside in. In place of a solid mass of rock which terminates upward in a narrow crest, the observer at the rim gazes down into an empty void, which terminates below in a narrow trough — the exact opposite of the crested ridge. The canyon suggests a mold in which mountain ranges might be cast.

In appearance the canyon is strange, memorable, unforgettable. It is ornately decorated and gorgeously adorned. Color is king. It is beyond easy comprehension or description. We struggle in vain for adequate words and expressions. Had the cradle of the race been near Grand Canyon, words and figures of speech might have come into being that would appropriately express the vigor and the expansive magnificence it exhibits. But as it is we may put away words and similes. There is nothing comparable to it. Grand Canyon is unspeakable!

The Grand Canyon, now admired by multitudes, was probably viewed by a white man for the first time when Cardenas gazed into its marvelous depths in the year 1540, probably near what is now called El Tovar. Most sightseers view it from nearly the same place — that is, from a point in northern Arizona where it may be reached by rail from the south. But this most advantageous place affords, it is generally thought, by no means the most glorious view.

First Impressions

The northern rim of the canyon is about 1,000 feet higher than the southern rim, and the most marvelous panoramas are to be seen from such vantage places as Point Sublime. But until recently the approach to the northern rim has been difficult. Although the superb views repay every effort they cost to the few who are fortunate enough to reach the northern rim, most travelers have been content with the view from the south. Here the gently undulating surface of the forest-covered Coconino Plateau, over which the canyon is approached, extends unbroken to the rim, where it gives place to rock walls that reach abruptly down into the great depths below.

This sudden change from the ordinary nearly level surface of the plateau to the precipitous faces of barren rock, descending, cliff after cliff, in seemingly endless succession down into the heart of the earth, is awe-inspiring to some and startling to others. Some are drawn to the rim as iron is drawn to the magnet, there to gaze in silent fascination; others become garrulous, uttering many an exclamation of wonder or amazement. Still others shrink back in timidity lest some invisible power draw them over the rim.

It is little wonder that the imaginative aborigines, who had no knowledge of the processes by which the great gorge was formed and no appreciation of its meaning, peopled the canyon with grotesque and diabolical spirits!

Let not the traveler think to take in Grand Canyon at a glance! Facts and impressions worth the gleaning require time. Long contemplation of the grand ensemble of stupendous mesas and buttes (Plate XVI), tributary gorges and amphitheaters, causes the eye to tire and the mind to flag. The observer can no more sense the Grand Canyon in an hour than he can gain in an hour the information to be obtained in a great museum.

If you have learned to admire the subdued natural scenery of New England, with its mild colors, its restful halftones, and its hazy vistas, lay that admiration reverently aside before you approach the Grand Canyon!

If you have learned to love the forested Adirondacks and their verdure-clothed valleys, or the rounded forms of the Appalachian Mountains, forget them before reaching the Grand Canyon, for such scenes are unknown here.

Even if you have learned to love the great symmetrical masses of granite in the Rocky Mountains or have seen the majestic monarchs of other mountain systems, with snowy crowns and cloudy halos, lay the mental picture resolutely aside before stepping out on the rim of Grand Canyon.

The canyon is different! In place of the rounded, graceful curves of eastern landscapes we see hard, angular, rocky forms, which stand out in striking boldness — forms that may at first seem grotesque and repellent rather than attractive. Here, in place of subdued colors gently blending in a hazy atmosphere, are brilliant, blazing colors, which, although somewhat mellowed by varying atmospheric effects, seem at first to carry with them something of the hardness of the rocks from which they emanate, for verdure is so scarce in the canyon walls as to be negligible and the atmosphere is too clear to give the softer atmospheric effects which the eastern artist strives to reproduce on canvas.

The Grand Canyon is not to be directly compared with other natural scenes. As the observer studies the great panorama from some point of vantage he may gradually learn to realize that what at first seemed harsh has a peculiar beauty and symmetry, and that each separate form in the great architectural ensemble has an attractiveness all its own.

Need of Study

The author who would write with intelligent enthusiasm of Grand Canyon must dwell in its presence long enough to gain some intimacy with it. The observer who fails at first glance to experience a rapturous exaltation may censure for exaggeration the writer who waxes enthusiastic.

It has been truthfully said that objects which disclose their full power and beauty as soon as they are presented to the mind have little of those qualities to disclose. Great innovations, whether in art or literature, in science or in nature, seldom take the world by storm. They must be understood before they can be rightly estimated and must be cultivated before they can be understood. The observer who would appreciate Grand Canyon must take time to understand it — and no man has yet exhausted its possibilities.

It is reserved for a favored few to stand on Point Sublime and view the wide landscape spread before them. There are many other almost equally commanding points on the north rim which afford unusually extensive views. These remain chiefly for enjoyment in the future. Vastly more than can be realized in the short time of an ordinary visit may be seen from any one of the many points in the south rim which may be reached easily.

At one of the points within easy walking distance of Grand Canyon Station, such as Hopi Point, we stand on the edge of the Coconino Plateau at an altitude of more than 7,000 feet above sea level and gaze downward over a succession of cliffs so precipitous that they seem to form an almost vertical face of rock terminated 3,500 feet below by a broad shelf preserved in the side of the canyon by a layer of hard rock and known as the Tonto Platform.

Jutting out from these cliffs and rising shelf on shelf above this platform are long, narrow tongues composed of brilliantly colored rock. Below this platform more than a thousand feet of ancient crystalline rock is exposed in the narrow sinuous trench called Granite Gorge, at the bottom of which flows Colorado River.

As seen from the rim the stream appears so minute and so feeble that an observer untrained in physiographic processes may receive with incredulity the statement that this little thread-like stream has carved out the enormous chasm which a whole chain of mountains would scarcely fill. But those who have intimate knowledge of this river know that it is a turbulent stream of great erosive power. One who stands on its brink in time of flood has no difficulty in understanding that the river dug the canyon.

One who is ascending a mountain passes through the same climatic zones that he would traverse in going northward at a low altitude. A traveler ascending one of the high mountains near the equator passes in succession from a tropical region through a temperate zone to an arctic zone at the top and encounters corresponding changes in plant and animal life. The reverse experience is felt by one who descends into Grand Canyon, for the cold-temperate climate at the rim changes to an almost tropical climate at the bottom.

Kaibab Plateau

The surface of the Kaibab Plateau, which lies north of the canyon in Arizona, reaches altitudes nearly 8,000 feet above sea level and has a climate comparable perhaps to the northern part of the Great Lakes region. Here at some places winter snow accumulates to a depth of 10 feet. Forests of yellow pine cover the uplands, and Engelmann's spruce covers the slopes. Here and there are groves of tangled scrub oak. Thickets of aspens, whose tall, silvery trunks are surmounted by scant tufts of tremulous leaves, are to be seen in many places. The constant nervous agitation of these leaves gives rise to the name quaking asp, by which the tree is commonly known. So richly is the turf covered with flowering plants in summer that 600 species have been collected by one man in a single season.

Coconino Plateau

The surface of the Coconino Plateau, south of the canyon, is about a thousand feet lower than that of the Kaibab, and, because of its lower altitude it has a milder climate and a different flora. Here the snows of winter rarely last a week, and a few of the summer days are unpleasantly warm. Juniper and piñon, or nut pine, are common. Some of the forest trees are dwarfed, and many of them are richly decorated with mistletoe, whose light green and yellowish shades contrast strongly with the dark green of the pines. In the more open spaces between the groves of forest trees are found such desert vegetation as the bunched sagebrush, "Mormon tea," cactus, and "mescal."

PLATE IX. A LANDSCAPE IN THE CLOUDS, SHOWING THE EASTERN FACE OF MOUNT WHITNEY, CALIFORNIA, THE HIGHEST PEAK IN THE UNITED STATES PROPER, AS SEEN FROM THE EAST.

This mountain, whose altitude is 14,898 feet, rises far above the timber line, and its slopes and cliffs consist of barren rock. The highest point, which appears in the center of the picture, is about 3,000 feet higher than the lake at the right. Photograph by Willis T. Lee.

PLATE X. MOUNT WHITNEY AND THE EASTERN ESCARPMENT OF THE SIERRA NEVADA IN CALIFORNIA, AS SEEN FROM AN AIRPLANE.

In no way except from a point in the air could this comprehensive view of the rugged mountain be obtained. Official photograph U. S. Army Air Service.

The Esplanade

The next climatic zone in descending order is that of the Esplanade, an irregular sloping shelf about a thousand feet below the south rim of the canyon, which is much more conspicuous a few miles farther downstream than it is near Hopi Point. Here the climate is notably milder than that on the plateau above and the flora takes on an aspect more nearly like that of a desert. There is a commingling of the plants of the temperate zone above and the more nearly tropical zone below.

The Tonto Platform

On descending to the Tonto Platform, about 3,500 feet below the south rim, a climate is found so mild that a fall of snow is almost unknown and the plants are chiefly those of an arid desert, such as "cats-claw," "red bud," and other small trees, and many species of cactus. The plants exhibit the spiny exterior, the aroma, the small leaf surface, the water-storing devices, and the somber hues of a desert flora.

The Inner Gorge

But it is in the inner gorge that a tropical climate is found. Here winter weather is rare and the summer sun makes the bottom of the canyon a veritable inferno. The winds at times are like blasts from a furnace. One of the most vivid recollections of my stay at Grand Canyon is a trip one winter's day on Bright Angel Trail. From the river, where we were uncomfortably warm, we passed upward through days of ideal weather until we reached a point a few hundred feet below the top. There we encountered snow, and finally we reached the rim in a driving storm, which had spread several inches of snow over the plateau during our absence.

How the Canyon Was Made

One of the first questions that arises in the mind of the observer is, How was Grand Canyon formed? Many an answer has been given — some plausible, some curiously ingenious, some picturesque, and some consisting only of poetic fancies that have no basis in fact.

Major Powell gives the Indians' conception of its origin as follows:

Long ago there was a great and wise chief, who mourned the death of his wife and would not be comforted until Ta-vwoats, one of the Indian gods, came to him and told him she was in a happier land, and offered to take him there, that he might see for himself, if upon his return he would cease to mourn. The great chief promised. Then Ta-vwoats made a trail through the mountains that intervene between that beautiful land, the balmy region in the great west, and this, the desert home of the poor Nu'-ma.

This trail was the canyon gorge of the Colorado. Through it Ta-vwoats led him; and when they had returned the deity exacted from the chief a promise that he would tell no one of the joys of that land, lest, through discontent with the circumstances of this world, they should desire to go to heaven. Then he rolled a river into the gorge, a mad, raging stream, that should engulf any who might attempt to enter it.

Little less fantastic, and lacking the saving poetic qualities of the aborigines' account, is the explanation of the Canyon as a great crack on the earth's crust formed by an earthquake.

Competent judges have but one explanation. The chasm is a product of erosion. Colorado River and its tributaries, aided by rain, frost, wind, and chemical action, have been at work age after age, cutting away the rock and carrying the waste material to or toward the sea.

As the process of erosion, or the wasting of the land, will here be referred to many times, a brief picture may be drawn to show how its results are accomplished. This is especially appropriate here because the canyon is the most conspicuous product of erosion to be found in all the world and because the river is cutting away the rock at the present time probably as fast as it ever did.

Great results may be accomplished by forces so insignificant that they escape the notice of unobservant persons. Some who have not given the subject special thought may read with incredulity the statement that great mountains are carved out largely by rain water. But those who understand the processes by which a landscape is shaped have long recognized the fact that rain is one of the principal means of erosion. Each raindrop picks up a tiny load of mud or sand, and the myriad drops collect to form rivulets, which join a river that carries great loads of mud to or toward the sea.

The late John Murray has shown that each year water equivalent in volume to many cubic miles falls on the earth as rain and that it carries into the sea about 2,735,000,000 tons of solid matter.

But probably work equal to that performed by water falling as rain is done by means of other agents. Water has been called a universal solvent. In spite of frequent references to "pure water" there is no such thing on the face of the earth. Water always carries mineral matter in solution. If it contains certain kinds in sufficient quantity it may be called a mineral water, but in reality the water of every spring, every well, and every stream holds mineral matter in solution.

The raindrop on its way from the cloud to the earth absorbs oxygen, carbon dioxide, and other gases, and on penetrating the soil takes up vegetable acids and various other ingredients. It carries these into the minute crevices of the rock, where chemical changes take place. The water is not so much the cause of the chemical action as it is the carrier of the chemical agents. Some of the newly formed compounds are easily soluble and are quickly taken into solution by the water; others are less soluble. Thus, through the agency of rain water, parts of the rocks are dissolved out and other parts are left, these parts being held together so loosely that the rock finally crumbles. The consideration of chemical solution and its results might be expanded into volumes, for it embraces many important processes, such as the production of soil, the formation of minerals, and the deposition and concentration of metalliferous ores.

The decay of rocks seems more conspicuous on lowlands and on gentle slopes than on highlands or on steep slopes such as those in Grand Canyon, because the removal of waste products goes on less vigorously there than on highlands. Also, where the rocks are bare, as in the steep walls of the canyon, relatively little water finds its way into them. Most of the rain escapes as surface run-off.

On the other hand, in regions where water may freeze at night and the ice melt by day, the water that enters the cracks and pores of the rock becomes an effective agent of destruction. As the water expands on freezing, the rock is fractured. A crack thus formed may be filled with water, which on freezing enlarges the crack. This may occur again and again until the loosened masses are finally pushed to positions where they fall when released by the melting ice. The fall of masses released in this way from exposed ledges is common in high mountains and in steep walls of canyons, where, after a night of frost, the morning sun weakens the hold of the ice on the loosened masses.

The chemical work of solutions in disintegrating the rocks and the mechanical work of frost in breaking them up would

PLATE XI. THE SOUTH SHORE OF CRATER LAKE, AS SEEN FROM THE WATCHMAN.

The water occupies a depression in the top of a mountain of volcanic origin. It is supposed that the mountain was built up over a quantity of hot lava and that the escape of this lava through some unknown passage allowed the top of the mountain to collapse. Photograph by Fred Kiser. Courtesy U. S. National Park Service.

Plate XII. Scene in Colorado National Monument; Remnants of Massive Red Sandstone 500 Feet High.

This sandstone, which geologists call the Wingate, is of Jurassic age. It is found throughout the plateau region, where it forms many of the curious and impressive erosion remnants of highly colored rock that have given to the plateau region the expressive name "The Natural Picture Gallery of the World." Photograph by Willis T. Lee.

have little effect in shaping a landscape if the products of their activity were not carried away. A relatively small amount of rock waste is carried away by wind; most of it is carried away by streams, which receive solutions of mineral matter and the smaller fragments of rock and transport them to the sea. The small particles remain suspended for a time, rendering the water turbid, and they may be carried for great distances down the stream before they find temporary lodgment in places along its course. The larger pieces of broken rock, such as boulders, pebbles, and sand, take shorter journeys. They are moved farther and farther downstream until they are ground to powder. Also in the course of their passage they scour the rocks they pass over.

The streams do actual cutting by rolling pebbles along the bottom and by scouring their beds with the mud and sand they hold in suspension, but the mechanical work done by ordinary streams is subordinate to their work of transportation. In streams where muddy water is whirled swiftly through rock channels, such as Colorado River in its passage through Grand Canyon, the cutting is at a maximum. In streams where the water is clear the abrasive work is negligible.

Ordinarily streams are inspected when their water is clear and they are doing little work. They do their cutting principally during times of flood, when the water is muddy. Particles of mud and grains of sand are carried downstream in endless procession, each particle doing its bit toward cutting away the rock.

Some observers who gaze into the Grand Canyon are content with the enigmatical statement that the chasm was "gnawed out by the tooth of time." Others are interested to know that the teeth which did the gnawing were the grains of sand that are set in the jaws of every flood.

Major Powell's Exploration

Major Powell, who conducted the famous exploration of the Grand Canyon, had implicit faith in the ability of these minute grains to accomplish great results. Many have marveled at the temerity shown by him and his daring associates in entering a canyon whose walls at many places rise sheer from the water, without knowing what falls they were likely to encounter. But Major Powell had observed that the water of the Colorado is always muddy, and he was convinced that great waterfalls are not to be expected in a muddy river. Such falls as may have existed there at one time had long ago been worn down by the myriads of sand grains which had passed over them. It is said that his faith in the efficiency of these minute agents of erosion was such that he staked his life on their ability to destroy falls.

Powell and others who followed him make frequent mention of falls in the canyon of the Colorado, where the river descends rapidly over heaps of boulders. These are rapids, as technically distinguished from falls. There are no cascades or cataracts on the Colorado — no place where the river pours with sheer drop over a ledge of rock.

How Mountains are Carried to the Sea

But even in a stream which is perpetually muddy, like Colorado River, the abrasive work is subordinate to the work of transportation. Water descends in the form of rain so quietly that we think little of the work it may accomplish. But the gathering of the rain water into myriads of streamlets which bear the small particles of sand and mud to the brook accomplishes enormous tasks. The water of the stronger current of the brook gathers still larger fragments of loose material and carries them to the river on their way to the sea.

Other parts of the rain water enter the rock and dissolve portions of it, and these in time find their way downstream, together with the mud. Every year the streams of the United States carry to the sea about 270,000,000 tons of dissolved mineral matter and 513,000,000 tons of suspended matter, such as silt and mud.

The rate at which streams work is influenced by many conditions, such as the velocity of flow, the character of the country they drain, and the climate, which determines whether the flow is constant, as in streams of a moist country, or intermittent, as in streams of a desert. On the average the surface of North America is lowered by erosion at the rate of one foot in about 9,000 years. If this erosive action of the streams of the United States could have been concentrated on the Isthmus of Panama it would have dug in about 73 days the canal which required 10 years' work with the most powerful appliances yet devised by man.

Although the energy of the river has been used chiefly in cutting downward into the rocks and in carving the plateau into a vast labyrinth of gorges, in any one of which the Niagara gorge would seem lost, there will probably come a time when the energy of the river will be expended chiefly in widening rather than in deepening the canyon — when the vast panorama of buttressed mesas and ornately decorated pinnacles will be swept away. It cannot cut downward below the level of its mouth, and a time may come, as it has come to many an older stream, when it can no longer cut downward. But it can and will continue to cut away its banks, undermine the canyon walls, and carry the débris to the sea. If this process is not interrupted the whole plateau will be swept away at some date in the inconceivably long time to come.

Will the process continue? Who can tell? During geologic ages long past the leveling process in this same region was carried to an extreme at least four times, and each time a plain of unknown extent was formed near sea level.

On the other hand, movement of a large part of the earth's crust or a variety of other causes may change the program, or even reverse the river's activity and cause it to deposit sediment and build up its bed, rather than to deepen its course and broaden it. At some places along its lower course the Colorado is filling its channel, which was once deeper than it is now, and during two periods of its history it filled its valley with sand and gravel to depths of hundreds of feet.

Power of Running Water

The fact that the river carries great loads of gravel and boulders was indelibly impressed on my mind several years ago, while I was engaged in work in northern Arizona. In addition to the numerous exploratory excursions overland it was my good fortune to take one by boat down the river from the mouth of the Grand Canyon to Yuma.

While I was at the mouth of the canyon, where the river emerges like a huge mill race from between the mile-high walls, the water began to rise and to increase the velocity of its flow. This increase disturbed the boulders that had lodged along the river's course and made them resume their interrupted journey toward the sea. The river here is perhaps 300 feet wide and 25 feet deep and is confined in a trough of solid rock. The gravel and boulders are washed through this trough with terrific force to find temporary lodgment in the more open spaces below the mouth of the canyon.

My attention was attracted by a peculiar muffled rumbling, which I did not at first understand. My thought at once turned to the sudden floods in Arizona with which I was familiar, where the dry sandy bed of a wash may suddenly and without obvious cause become a raging torrent; the cause,

PLATE XIII. LONGS PEAK AND LONGS PEAK INN.

Longs Peak (altitude 14,255 feet), the highest point in Rocky Mountain National Park, appears in the center between Mount Meeker, at the left, and Mount Lady Washington, at the right. In the middle is The Chasm, a depression 2,312 feet deep, in which Mills Glacier originated. The moraine of the old glacier appears on the mountain slope as an elongated crescent-shaped ridge nearly 1,000 feet high, consisting of fragments of rock carried by the ancient glaciers out of The Chasm. Photograph by Willis T. Lee.

Plate XIV. View Northward across Grand Canyon from the End of Grand Scenic Divide.

SC, Shinumo Creek; V, Vishnu schist; B, Bass limestone; H, Hakatai shale; Sh, Shinumo quartzite; D, Dox sandstone; d, diabase intrusive; T, Tapeats sandstone; BA, Bright Angel shale; M, Mauv limestone; R, Redwall limestone; Ss, sandstone of Supai formation; Ssh, shale of Supai formation; C, Coconino sandstone; K, Kaibab limestone; WK, West Kaibab fault. Photograph by N. W. Carkhuff.

a sudden downpour of rain at some distant point hours before, may have been forgotten or may have been beyond the range of vision.

I did not then know the Colorado as well as I know it now, and, fearing a sudden rise in the water, my boatmen hastily secured the boat and we climbed up the banks for safety. I made my way along a shelf of rock into a narrow part of the gorge and there discovered the cause of our alarm. The swift current was rolling boulders through the rock trough.

My shelf of rock was perhaps 10 feet above the water and the boulders in the turbid flood below were crashing and grinding against the rock walls. Reason told me that I was perfectly safe — that thousands of floods had rolled boulders through the trough without injury to the shelf on which I stood. But of what use is reason at such a time? Precaution (or perhaps it should be called fear) argued that "some time this shelf will fall, and maybe that time is now!" A score of reasons were marshalled why I should leave that particular shelf forthwith.

The Colorado River within the Grand Canyon averages about 300 feet in width and 30 feet in depth, and has a mean velocity of about 2 miles an hour. The drainage from large parts of five States swells the volume of its flow. And what may be said of the volume of rock waste that its muddy waters have transported to the sea? The volume might be computed but the figures would be incomprehensible.

Unmeasured quantities of mud and sand have been washed down its course from the Rocky Mountains, for it rises in the heart of these mountains in the Rocky Mountain National Park. Unmeasured quantities of mud and sand have found their way from the mountains and plains of Wyoming down its rocky trough. Thicknesses of rock measured by thousands of feet have been removed from the plateaus of Utah, Colorado,

New Mexico, and Arizona, and the products have passed in endless procession down the river to the sea.

From thousands of square miles thousands of feet of rock have been removed by the river. What has become of it all? Those who have crossed the built-up plains and the filled valleys of Arizona and southeastern California have seen some of it, for these level plains occupy the site of old valleys filled to the brim and overflowing with gravel, sand, and mud from mountains, plains, and plateaus hundreds of miles away.

Those who have traveled over the Southern Pacific railroad in southern California, where this road crosses the broad delta which the Colorado built out across the Gulf of California so far that the north end of the depression now occupied by Salton Sea was completely cut off from the southern part, have seen some of it. But what of the rest? As well ask what has become of a life that is spent! It has passed down the river, it has done its bit toward accomplishing a great task, and has vanished — *somewhere.*

Rocks of Grand Canyon

It has been rightly said that the Grand Canyon offers the most instructive exhibit of geology in the world. This is true because, in cutting the great trench through the plateau, the river has exposed to view in profile rocks more than a mile thick, ranging in age from the oldest (the Archean) to the youngest and representing nearly all of the great periods of geologic time. Expressed in another way, the time represented by the rocks which the eye takes in at a glance is many thousands of times greater than the popularly accepted duration of the life of the human race.

In the walls of the canyon are seen the edges of a succession of sedimentary rocks lying layer upon layer, each of uniform thickness and character, extending as far as the eye can reach and nearly horizontal in position, like sheets of cardboard laid one upon another.

These layers of rock differ in kind and in character. Some are composed of sand and shale, others of limestone. Some are red, a color due to the presence of oxide of iron, or iron rust. Others are green or gray or white. The softer layers break down readily and form slopes, the harder ones resist erosion and stand out as cliffs. The rim is composed of hard limestone about 600 feet thick, which contains fossil sea shells.

Rocks like individuals, may be conveniently referred to by name. This limestone has been named Kaibab and was christened for Kaibab Plateau, which it caps. The next lower layer is a 300-foot gray, conspicuously cross-bedded sandstone, the Coconino, which forms cliffs and appears as a narrow light-colored band near the top of the canyon walls. Next below is a group of rocks consisting of layers of red sandstone separated by layers of soft red shale. It is called the Supai formation, which is 1200 to 1400 feet thick. The soft layers break down readily and form sloping surfaces; the hard layers form benches.

The next thick layer of rocks, in order downward, is the hard Redwall limestone, the most conspicuous cliffmaker in Grand Canyon. Between this limestone and the granite below are the soft, shaly beds of the Tonto group, which have been worn back to form the Tonto platform. The lowest layer of this group is a hard brown pebbly sandstone, which makes the floor of the platform.

The oldest rocks exposed at the bottom of the chasm are the ancient crystallines called Archean. In some places, but not in all, between these oldest rocks and those of the Tonto group there are remnants of a great series of sediments which probably represents as much or even more of the earth's history than all the other rocks above put together. And yet most of this great series of beds was worn away before the sediments of the Tonto group were laid down. The contact of these younger rocks with the older where the intermediate rocks were removed is known as an unconformity.

Ancient Lands and Unconformities

The sediments of the rocks exposed in the walls of the canyon were not laid down continuously. At some places long periods of time elapsed after one layer was finished before the overlying layer was begun. Some of these intervals were so long that mountain systems were formed and later worn away before sediments were again laid down there. For the history of events during this interval we must look in other parts of the earth.

The scenes in the plateau region, the most remarkable of which are found in Grand Canyon, are results of a long series of events, which extend far back into the dim ages before life was begun. Hence it may be said that the older rocks of the canyon have witnessed the development of the earth from a mass that was "without form and void" — at least without the external form that it now has — and void of any of the forms of plant life that now beautify it and of the animals that inhabit it.

These older rocks were buried by sand, mud, and limy ooze, much of which was deposited in sea water during the time when the plateau region, now between one and two miles high, was below sea level. At other times the region was above water and the deposits were partly, and in places wholly, cut away by wave and stream. The parts which escaped destruction constitute the record from which the history of the region may be deciphered.

Geology and the Interpretation of Natural Scenery

This is not the place for a detailed account of the many events in the growth and development of the canyon region. It is rather a place to point the way to delve further into the great store of information which here invites the student who is interested in natural objects.

The interpretation of a landscape depends on a knowledge of the forces which produced it. As the rocks exposed in the canyon country range in age from the very youngest to the very oldest known on the face of the earth, an adequate interpretation of the scenery here may involve a knowledge of the whole range of historical geology, as well as a knowledge of physiography, or the science which teaches how landscapes are formed. For in geologic history one is dealing with a long succession of landscapes, a moving picture of the ages, in which the scene changes from time to time. Mountains rise out of the sea; are immediately attacked by the agents of erosion; are sculptured into peak and ridge, gorge and valley; are worn down and leveled; and finally are again covered by the sea. The canyon region was thus elevated, worn down, and resubmerged again and again in the course of its history.

Chapter IV

ANCIENT LANDSCAPES

From a geologist's point of view the Grand Canyon is of recent origin — that is, Colorado River may have begun its work of digging the canyon less than a million years ago. But the rocks exposed in it and in other parts of the Plateau country represent many an ancient landscape. Some of these date back so far that it is useless to speculate as to their age. Their antiquity may be stated, not in years, but in milleniums of centuries.

The crystalline rocks of the inner gorge were formed amid scenes wholly different from any that are familiar to us. So far as we know now, there were then no plants or animals. But storms raged and streams flowed then as now, and the lifeless landscape shaped by them is represented by an uneven plain, which separates the crystalline rocks from the younger sedimentary rocks that rest upon them. This plain is marked in the walls of the canyon by what is known to geologists as an unconformity.

The plain which shows as a line at the junction of the ancient crystalline and the overlying sedimentary rocks was at one time the surface. On it gathered the material of the younger rocks. The old crystalline rocks, called Archean because of their great age, have lain in their present buried position through the uncounted ages that have elapsed since they were thus entombed. During this time mountains have been thrown up and slowly eroded away, seas have swept over the scene and vanished, and whole groups of living beings have developed, run their course, and disappeared.

A Lifeless Landscape

If this book had been written a few years ago, before the nebular hypothesis had been seriously questioned, the statement would probably have been made that the crystalline rocks at the bottom of the canyon are parts of the earth's crust formed when it originally cooled from a molten state. But, as the planetesimal hypothesis, referred to at some length in a later chapter, has proved acceptable to some who believe that there never has been any original crust covering a general liquid interior, we may look for a possible alternative explanation of the crystalline character of the Archean rocks. Two explanations seem possible.

Rocks similar to the ancient crystallines of Grand Canyon have been traced laterally into rocks that are clearly of sedimentary origin. In such places the crystalline character is due to changes in the sediments after they were laid down. Second, in many places rocks are found which represent matter forced in a molten condition into previously solidified rocks. It is not always possible to determine whether a given mass of crystalline rock originated as sediments or as intrusive rock. However they may have originated, the old Archean rocks of the canyon were in place long ages ago, before life as we know it began on the earth.

The geologist is asked frequently when and how life began. There have been many speculations, some of them centuries old. But, after summing up all the wisdom of philosophers from the days of Moses to the present time it may be frankly admitted that we are not far beyond the statement that "in the beginning God created."

But although the Archean landscape was not adorned by any plant or animated by any form of life such as we are now familiar with, the processes of nature were probably in operation in much the same way that they are now, for during the time that intervened between the period represented by these ancient rocks and those of the succeeding Algonkian time, mountains were raised and these in turn were cut down and swept into the sea. The destruction of mountains and the formation of plains such as that which we can trace between the old crystallines and the younger rocks were accomplished then, as they are now, by the action of rain, stream, wind, and wave.

Archean Time

Less is known of the Archean than of any other geologic period. In this respect it is comparable to the prehistoric stage in human history, concerning which there are legends and myths, inferences and guesses, but no written records. The inferences under the nebular hypothesis as to the early history of the earth are well known, as they have been portrayed by many a fantastic word-picture.

But the planetesimal hypothesis is new, hence the possible course of events under it which culminated in the formation of such rocks as the ancient crystallines of Grand Canyon is not so well known. The story of the development of the earth under this hypothesis is quite different from that of the supposed development under the older hypothesis. The chief events may be enumerated as follows (fuller descriptions may be found in the writings of Prof. T. C. Chamberlin):

According to the planetesimal hypothesis, there was a time when the young earth, only a small fraction of its present size, was without form or at least had a very indefinite form and was growing rapidly by the fall of particles of matter or planetesimals attracted to it from surrounding space. This young earth had no water and no atmosphere, because the attractive force of the small mass was not strong enough to hold the gases of air and water.

PLATE XV. LOOKING INTO GRAND CANYON FROM THE AIR.

In the upper left-hand corner appears the even surface of hard rock at the top of the plateau in which the canyon is eroded. Below the rim appear the slopes of soft rock and the cliffs of hard rock. Official photograph U. S. Army Air Service.

In time, when the nucleus had grown by accretion or the addition of solid particles to something like one-tenth of the present mass of the earth, it began to gather an atmosphere, because then its attractive force was able to hold the gases. The moon ($\frac{1}{81}$ of the earth's mass) has no atmosphere, but Mars (about $\frac{1}{9}$ of the earth's mass) has a thin atmosphere. When the growing earth had become large enough to hold by its attractive force the swiftly moving particles of oxygen, nitrogen, and water vapor, and prevent them from escaping into space, these gases began to accumulate and form an atmosphere. The heavy gases of slow movement, such as carbonic acid gas, may have been captured first; the lighter and swifter ones later, when the earth was larger and had greater attractive force. But the earth is not large enough yet to capture and hold hydrogen and helium, although it might hold these gases in its atmosphere should it grow sufficiently large, for these gases exist in the atmosphere of the sun.

The rocks, cold at first, may have been heated by impact in the fall of the planetesimals, by compression, by internal friction of the compressed masses under gravitative force, or by other processes, less easily understood. Probably it cannot be proved that no large part of the earth was ever molten at one time, but the fact that it is now as solid as steel harmonizes with the belief that the earth has never been a molten globe and that it has never possessed the high temperatures at the surface which the nebular hypothesis demands.

When the atmosphere had gathered enough water vapor to become saturated, precipitation began. Previous to this time there were no streams, lakes, or seas. The rain water falling on the surface naturally dissolved the more soluble material and carried it in solution into the depressions of the earth's surface, just as it does today. Also, just as today, the water evaporated, leaving the soluble salts in the basins. Thus the

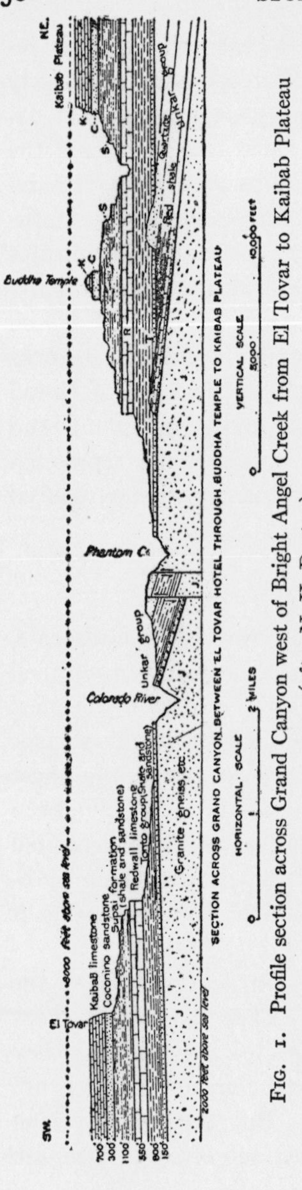

Fig. 1. Profile section across Grand Canyon west of Bright Angel Creek from El Tovar to Kaibab Plateau (after N. H. Darton).

hollows at first held fresh-water lakes, which gradually increased in volume and salinity through uncounted ages until they became great briny oceans.

If this process began when the earth was only as large as Mars its outer shell, about 1900 miles thick, grew up in the presence of water, and to the salinity of the ocean nine tenths of the earth's mass has contributed part of its soluble matter. In this connection also it may be noted that in place of a universal ocean, which, according to the older belief, covered the face of the earth, the newer notion postulates universal land, from the higher parts of which streams washed rock débris into basins that finally became filled with lakes and seas. Also under the newer hypothesis there is no reason for believing that the climate of these very early stages in the development of the earth was greatly different from that of later time.

The succession of events in the growth of the earth, as stated, gives no grounds for supposing that living beings could not exist very early in its history. Some of the oldest forms of life known (the crustaceans whose fossil remains are obtained from rocks of Algonkian age) stand relatively high in the scale of animal life. Living beings must have existed for long ages in order to be developed into animals of the high order of these crustaceans. The observed facts demand conditions favorable to life for a long time prior to the Algonkian period, and the succession of events just outlined indicates that such conditions may have prevailed during the period represented by the Archean rocks at the bottom of Grand Canyon.

The plainly defined line of unconformity between the rocks of Archean age and those next younger in the walls of Grand Canyon — separating the Unkar from the underlying granite and gneiss — is shown in Figure 1. This unconformity represents a long period of erosion, during which the region was reduced to a nearly level plain.

The Algonkian Period

This Archean plain was submerged and covered by sediments, deposited chiefly in water. The epoch of deposition continued until the sediments had in some places gathered to a thickness of about 12,000 feet. In other places, however, the surface was above water and was being worn down to supply these sediments. Some of the material is coarse and may have been deposited along streams; some of it is fine and was deposited as mud in shallow water; and some is limestone, which probably accumulated when the site of Grand Canyon was beneath the sea.

These rocks differ in character and appearance from the younger rocks which overlie them. They are changed or metamorphosed. When they were deposited as sediments they did not differ from the sand, mud, and limy ooze which are being deposited at the present time. But through the long ages that have elapsed they have been subjected to pressure and heat. They have been fractured, and molten rock has been forced into them. They have begun the change by which they may at some time in the future attain the crystalline condition of the Archean rocks beneath them.

Algonkian Glaciers

Little is known of the climate of Algonkian time, for the climate of a geologic period must be judged chiefly by its fossils. The living beings of Algonkian time consisted mainly of low types of marine animals and plants, such as seaweeds and worms, and relatively little is known of them.

But there is some convincing evidence concerning the Algonkian climate. Certain deposits indicate the presence of glaciers in Algonkian time, perhaps during more than one epoch, for the period was a long and varied one. Evidences of Algonkian glaciation have been found in Canada, Australia, India, China, South Africa, Europe, and elsewhere. Hence there is good reason for believing that the climate during this period was not greatly different from that of later time, and that instead of sweltering in a murky atmosphere of steam and heated gas, as some have supposed, the earth seems to have been colder on the average than now. Even in some equatorial regions it was clothed in ice during parts of this very early period.

After the deposition of the Grand Canyon series of strata there was extensive uplift and disturbance of the rocks, during which the material originally laid down in horizontal sheets was warped and tilted and broken into blocks. These blocks were faulted or moved out of place and the whole disturbed mass was eroded until at some places the Algonkian rocks were entirely swept away. At other places certain parts of them were preserved by being depressed below the level where erosion is possible, and some low hills were left where unusually hard rock cropped out.

PLATE XVI. EROSION FORMS IN THE GRAND CANYON DISTRICT AS SEEN FROM AN AIRPLANE. VIEW NEAR THE HOPE INDIAN RESERVATION, ON LITTLE COLORADO RIVER.

The photograph shows the buttes and mesas of the arid West. Official photograph U. S. Army Air Service 53781.

This series of events is known collectively as the Grand Canyon revolution. If the process of erosion by which the Grand Canyon was formed should continue until the river had swept away the whole plateau and formed a plain near sea level where the mile-high mesas now stand, the work accomplished would be less than that performed during the period of erosion which followed the Algonkian, for a thickness of more than 12,000 feet of rock was removed at that time.

Length of Algonkian Time

This great length of time, which has been regarded by some geologists as equal in duration to that of the ten great geologic periods ranging from Cambrian to the present day, is represented in some places in the canyon walls by a single line. Where the older rocks were tilted before they were eroded and covered with younger sediments the line represents what is called an angular unconformity, because the bedding planes of the older rocks meet those of the younger at an angle, as shown in the sections in Figure 1, such as that between the Unkar and the overlying shale. Where no angularity is apparent the line represents what is called an unconformity by erosion. In either case the line marks a break in deposition covering a period of time not represented by sedimentary rocks. It represents a period when records were being destroyed by the wasting away of the rock. Records of some of the periods unrecorded here are found in other parts of the world, for the rocks torn from the highlands in one place must find rest in some other place. But during the post-Algonkian period of erosion the continental areas of the whole world seem to have been high, so that the unconformity appears to be world-wide. This hiatus or break in recorded time is the greatest known, unless it is exceeded by that represented by the erosional unconformity between the Archean and Algonkian. Thus the two greatest unconformities in the world are represented in Grand Canyon, and both merge into a single unconformity at the base of the Tonto group, where the rocks of this group rest on the granite.

The Cambrian Period

The Cambrian is one of the long periods in the life of the earth and may be compared to a year in the life of man. The name was given by geologists to rocks that were first studied in Wales, a country known to the Romans as Cambria. Later, when it was learned that rocks were formed in other countries at the same time, the name Cambrian was applied to them also.

The Archean has been likened to the prehistoric age of human history, comparable in a sense to the old stone age, and the Algonkian to the legendary age, comparable to the period of Greek mythology. With the Cambrian period, represented by the Tonto group of the Grand Canyon, begins the stage of well-recorded geologic history. To carry the simile a step farther, this new era, like many in human history, began with a revolution called the Grand Canyon revolution. It is a modern era in earth history, for the Cambrian is said to date back only about a hundred million years, whereas the preceding periods date back infinitely farther.

There may have been some land plants of low order at this time, but the known plants of the Cambrian period are algæ or seaweeds. Although little is known of Cambrian plant life it must have been abundant, for animals depend on plants for food, and the animals of Cambrian time were numerous. They were low in the scale of life and were sea dwellers. No remains of land animals have been found and no vertebrates, even of the lowest type. Thus at the time the Tonto beds of Grand Canyon were forming there were sea worms, mollusks, sponges, and several low forms of life that were wholly unlike any now living. Some of these were preserved as fossils.

Fossils and History

Fossils are the symbols in which the history of the world's life is written, and a knowledge of the symbols is necessary before the story can be read. Animals and plants that lived long ago were buried in mud just as those of today are being so buried in some places. The mud hardened to rock and was covered in turn by other layers of mud. Some of these layers were lifted and eroded when the mountains were pushed up, exposing again the remains of the buried animals and plants. These remains are the characters in which some of the story of the earth is written. But the language must be known before the story can be translated.

If you look carefully at the shell of a living oyster you will observe certain definite features. You could not mistake it for anything else. Many things have been learned about the habits and life of this oyster. In some places it thrives; in others it cannot live. It is at home in a sheltered bay where the great waves of the ocean cannot disturb it, but is not happy in deep water far from shore. It cannot live long in fresh water and is happiest where the water is not so salty as in the open ocean.

If now we compare this shell with a fossil oyster shell we see that the two are similar. The one was found in Chesapeake Bay, the other in solid rock perhaps a mile above sea level and a thousand miles from any place where an oyster could now live, yet there is no doubt that the fossil is the shell of an oyster, and there should be no question that oysters thrive only in bodies of water connected with the sea.

Records in Stone

The fossil oyster shell tells us just as plainly as if the story were written in words that the place where it was found was once a mile lower than it is now and that the sea once occupied the region where it was found. It is evident also that in that olden time the streams were carrying sand and mud into the sea just as they are carrying them into the sea in our day. The mud hardened into rock, and this rock, once at the bottom of the sea, was in time pushed up with others to form mountains.

Nature not only wrote her story in plain language, but she arranged it in regular order, so that it can be divided into what we may call chapters. These are the geologic ages, such as the Cambrian. But although a complete story was written, not all parts of it can be found in any one place. Some can be found only in Europe, others only in America; some can be read only in the frozen lands of the Eskimo, others only in the Tropics. Not all of its parts have been found. Some may yet be recovered, but others may not, for the agents of destruction have been as busy in the past as they are in the present, and they have destroyed many records.

The rocks seen in the canyon walls above the Tonto group are of Devonian and Carboniferous age. They are younger than those of the Tonto formation by many millions of years. This long stretch of time, here unrecorded by deposition, is marked in the canyon walls by an unconformity. This unconformity differs from that found below the rocks of Cambrian age in two significant ways. The Tonto beds were not planed off, nor were they entirely removed at any place that is now exposed. The canyon region may have been above sea level during the time represented by the unconformity and may have received no sediments; or sedimentary rocks may have been formed here and later eroded away. However this may be, it is evident that the Cambrian rocks in this region were not crumpled up into mountains and that they were not raised far above sea level, otherwise they would have been deeply eroded or entirely removed.

Evidently the region lay low throughout all the time between the end of the Cambrian period and the beginning of the Carboniferous; in other words, the Ordovician and Silurian periods are not represented, and the Devonian is represented only in part, by thin beds, which are not readily distinguished from the overlying rocks.

The Carboniferous Period

Next above the Devonian and resting on it, or on the Cambrian rocks where the Devonian is absent, is a great layer of limestone, which is about 600 feet thick in the southern part of the canyon region and much thicker farther north. This limestone is harder than the rocks above and below it and has resisted erosion more strongly than they. It crops out midway in the canyon walls, where it forms bold, red promontories. Because of its color and the wall-like face of the cliffs it is called the Redwall limestone. It forms prominent cliffs in Cheops Pyramid and in several of the so-called temples, many of which are familiar to visitors in Grand Canyon National Park.

The Sea and Grand Canyon

Although the wall formed by this limestone is red, the rock itself is light blue or gray. Its color is due chiefly to wash from the red shale and sandstone above. This limestone contains fossil shells of sea animals and these fossils tell us that the Grand Canyon region, which had been above sea level during much of the time since the Cambrian period, subsided during the Carboniferous and was covered with sea water.

During the early part of the period represented by the Redwall limestone, sea water covered broad areas of the interior part of North America. Later in the period, although there was an open sea in the Grand Canyon region, broad swamps formed at many places in the interior of North America, and in these swamps accumulated the vegetable matter which formed the Carboniferous coal. Rocks of this age, both in America and in other continents, contain quantities of coal so vast that they are often called the Coal Measures. The name Carboniferous was suggested by the carbon of the coal.

The rocks above the Redwall limestone, the Supai red beds, 1,400 feet thick; the Coconino sandstone, 300 feet thick, which outcrops high in the canyon walls and which usually forms a nearly vertical cliff; and the Kaibab limestone, 600 feet thick, which forms the rim of the canyon in the National Park, were formed late in Carboniferous time.

Through geologic work in the canyon country we are continually learning more about the rocks in which the canyon is carved. It is now known that the beds formerly called Supai consist of two parts separated by an unconformity and the name Supai is today restricted to the lower part. The upper part is called the Hermit shale and is classed with the Coconino sandstone and the Kaibab limestone as Permian. But as this subdivision is likely to interest few besides professional geologists the older usage is here allowed to stand.

This series of rocks is clearly and beautifully exposed in the southern part of the canyon region, but it is not so clearly exposed in some other parts. North of Marble Canyon it is difficult to identify some of these formations. Parties sent out in recent years by the United States Geological Survey have obtained valuable additional information, which, however, has not yet been published, hence the old nomenclature is presented here.

PRINCIPAL DIVISIONS OF GEOLOGIC TIME.[a]

Era	Period	Epoch	Characteristic life
Cenozoic (recent life)	Quaternary	Recent Pleistocene (Great Ice Age)	"Age of man." Animals and plants of modern types.
	Tertiary	Pliocene Miocene Oligocene Eocene	"Age of mammals." Possible first appearance of man. Rise and development of highest orders of plants.
Mesozoic (intermediate life)	Cretaceous	(b)	"Age of reptiles." Rise and culmination of huge land reptiles (dinosaurs), of shell-fish with complexly partitioned coiled shells (ammonites), and of great flying reptiles. First appearance (in Jurassic) of birds and mammals; of cycads, an order of palmlike plants (in Triassic); and of angiospermous plants, among which are palms and hardwood trees (in Cretaceous).
	Jurassic	(b)	
	Triassic	(b)	
Paleozoic (old life)	Carboniferous	Permian	"Age of amphibians." Dominance of club mosses (lycopods) and plants of horsetail and fern types. Primitive flowering plants and earliest cone-bearing trees. Beginnings of backboned land animals (land vertebrates). Insects. Animals with nautilus-like coiled shells (ammonites) and sharks abundant.
		Pennsylvanian	
		Mississippian	
	Devonian	(b)	"Age of fishes." Shellfish (mollusks) also abundant. Rise of amphibians and land plants.
	Silurian	(b)	Shell-forming sea animals dominant, especially those related to the nautilus (cephalopods). Rise and culmination of the marine animals sometimes known as sea lilies (crinoids) and of giant scorpion-like crustaceans (eurypterids). Rise of fishes and of reef-building corals.
	Ordovician	(b)	Shell-forming sea animals abundant, especially cephalopods and mollusk-like brachiopods. Culmination of the buglike marine crustaceans known as trilobites. First trace of insect life.
	Cambrian	(b)	Trilobites and brachiopods most characteristic animals. Seaweeds (algæ) abundant. No trace of land animals found.
Proterozoic (primordial life)	Algonkian	(b)	First life that has left distinct record. Crustaceans, brachiopods, and seaweeds.
	Archean	Crystalline rocks	No fossils found.

a Many of the time divisions shown above are separated by unconformities — that is, the dividing lines in the table represent local or widespread uplifts or depressions of the earth's surface.
b Epoch names omitted; in less common use than those given.

Carboniferous Life

The first animals lived in the sea. But in Carboniferous time the higher forms of life became air breathers and lived on land. It has aptly been said that during this period life rose from the sea and took possession of the land. Little is known of the land forms of earlier ages, but the broad lowlands and swamps of Carboniferous time were favorable to the growth of land plants and to the development of animals that subsist on such plants.

The trees were altogether different from those of the present day (Plate XXI). There were among them some cycads — a type that culminated in a later age — and some conifers. There were also giant reeds called *Calamites*, and the ferns of that day grew to be large trees. But the dominant forest trees of Carboniferous time have no living representatives, hence no common name. There was *Lepidodendron*, a great tree that began life in an earlier geologic age and died out in the Permian epoch, at the end of the Carboniferous period. Some of these trees grew to be 100 feet in height and 3 or 4 feet in diameter. Their great pithy trunks of porous material — it can not properly be called wood — forking into a few prongs, were clothed with small evergreen leaves. Another common tree of this time is *Sigillaria*, distinguishable from *Lepidodendron* by parallel rows of leaf scars that ran straight up the fluted trunk, for those of *Lepidodendron* ran in spirals around the trunk.

With the lower orders of plants came the lower orders of insects, such as spiders, dragon-flies, and beetles, but no bees or ants, for there were no flowering plants, on which the higher insects live. About a thousand species of Carboniferous insects have been found, half of which are cockroaches. They may have been as harmless as their repulsive descendants, but we may give a sigh of relief and a smile of complacent satisfaction with present conditions when we reflect that some of the Carboniferous cockroaches were 4 inches long. We may also feel the same sense of relief in respect to the other insects, some of which, such as the dragon-fly, had a spread of wing of more than 2 feet.

Rise of Animals from Water to Land

The amphibians, which are sometimes defined as those vertebrates which made the transition from aquatic to terrestrial life, began at an early stage in the history of life and developed into true air-breathers. Their evolution during long ages is reproduced in miniature in the individual development of modern amphibians, such as toads and frogs, which begin life as purely aquatic gill-breathing creatures and later become air-breathers. The amphibians and the reptiles, which began their existence in Coal Measures time, were the most highly developed beings of that age. They were very different from the living forms, and some of them were as large as crocodiles. The development of these air-breathing vertebrates is regarded as the most important event in the whole progress of evolution, for it represents the rise of animal life out of the water. From the Carboniferous period to the present time the air-breathers have been the dominant forms of living creatures.

The climate of the Coal Measures period seems to have been warm and moist, and the growing season seems to have lasted the year round. Coal beds on the Antarctic continent and also far to the north, as well as coral reefs in Spitzbergen, indicate that a warm climate then extended nearly to both poles. A picture of the monotonous Carboniferous landscape is drawn by Charles Schuchert as follows:

> In these forests of Pennsylvanian time might have been seen flying about the largest insects that have ever lived, — great dragonflies reaching a wing spread of over 2 feet. Huge cockroaches abounded everywhere in great variety, giants of four inches in

length not being rare. As a rule these insects were carnivorous and did not transfer the pollen from one flower to another, as is so commonly done by living insects among present-day plants. The smaller forms were preyed upon by scorpions or spiders, the latter not making webs but living on the ground or in rotten logs along with many myriapods or thousand-legs. No insect of this kind, so far as known, produced chirping or other sounds and the soughing of the wind among the trees was possibly rarely interrupted, save by the croak of an amphibian in the marsh. Reptiles and amphibians were common in the swamps, and it is probable that many small reptiles were running over the ground and about the trees. No large land animals such as we know and no birds were to be seen.

Most of the rocks of Carboniferous age in the Grand Canyon were formed in water, but in many parts of the world rocks of this age contain beds of coal, which renders appropriate the name Carboniferous.

While the limy ooze was gathering in the sea in northern Arizona, broad swamps were forming at many places in central and eastern North America and in many other parts of the world. In these swamps accumulated the vegetable matter which formed the coal of this age.

The Formation of Coal

Most of the coal now used in America is mined in the eastern and central fields, or between Pennsylvania and Kansas, where, in an area of 214,686 square miles, the coal stored in beds thick enough for mining and near enough to the surface to be reached in mines has been estimated at 1,142,340,000,000 tons. If the coal of all the geologic ages should be included in the estimate the United States has 496,776 square miles of coal land and a supply of 3,157,243,000,000 tons.

Nearly all coal beds represent ancient swamps in which vegetable matter accumulated, as it does now, in standing water, where it partly decomposes to form muck and peat. The peat undergoes certain changes, is packed or consolidated by the weight of the sediments that gather on it, and becomes lignite, a soft near-coal whose woody character may easily be distinguished. The process by which peat is changed through lignite and bituminous coal to anthracite and finally to graphite is somewhat similar to the production of coke from coal, by which some constituents are converted into gas and driven off, leaving much of the carbon in the form called coke. This change of peat to anthracite may be caused by natural heat, but in many places it seems to have been caused rather by pressure and warping of the rocks, together, perhaps, with such heat as was caused by this warping.

A Measure of Geologic Time

The rate of accumulation of carboniferous material has been made the basis for computing the age of the rocks which contain the coal. It has been estimated[1] that under the best conditions enough vegetable matter may be produced on a tract of land in about 300 years to make a coal bed one foot thick covering the same tract, provided none of it is lost. On the assumption that coal was produced in Carboniferous time at the same rate, the accumulation of the maximum thickness of 300 feet of coal in the Appalachian basin required 90,000 years. Naturally the rate of plant growth during the Carboniferous period is not known, nor is it known what proportion of the plants decayed at the surface or for any other reason was not included in the mass that was buried and turned to coal. But the figures seem to indicate that probably much more than 90,000 years was consumed in forming the beds of coal. This takes no account of the time required for the accumulation of the thousands of feet of sedimentary rock in which the coal was embedded.

Another way of arriving at the approximate length of a

[1] Ashley, Geo. H., Economic Geology, p. 47, 1907.

geologic period is by the rate of accumulation of rock material. Some geologists have estimated that in regions where coral reefs abound limy mud (calcium carbonate) may accumulate at such a rate that a foot of limestone would be formed in 200 years. In regions where calcium carbonate is precipitated chemically, with little aid from organisms, its accumulation may be very much slower, possibly less than a foot in 1,000 years. This rate may be used in illustrating the method of reaching an approximation of geologic time but should not be used as if based on a secure foundation. If the Redwall limestone was formed at this rate, the thickness of 600 feet represents 600,000 years. Its massive nature and the scarcity of fossils in it suggests slow accumulation and correspondingly long time.

Several methods have been used to reach a measure of geologic time. The most recent one is based on radio-activity, and this method indicates surprising lengths of time. On this subject Dr. W. H. McNairn [1] says:

> Among those elements which are known to undergo the mysterious change due to disintegration of the atom is uranium. By giving off particles of helium at a constant and definite rate, uranium is believed to pass over into radium and lead. If in any given uranium-bearing mineral we can determine the relative proportions of uranium, radium, and helium, and lead if it is present, knowing the rate at which these changes take place, we should be able to determine the age of the mineral itself.
>
> This method, first suggested by Sir Ernest Rutherford in 1906, was subsequently made good by the Honorable R. J. Strutt. His results were somewhat startling in the unexpectedly great periods of time which they indicated. For instance, he allotted the very respectable antiquity of 141,000,000 years to some rocks which were found about half-way down to the earliest fossiliferous deposits. However, these first figures were not uniform. Of recent years these have been tabulated and indicate a certain amount of con-

[1] McNairn, W. H., The Scientific American Supplement, April 19, 1919.

sistency, particularly in their unanimity in extending the reach of geological time to an extent undreamed of by the geologists. Who, for example, would have dared to suggest, from geological evidence alone, that we have to do with periods of from 800 to 1,600 million years?

The Permian Epoch

The Permian epoch takes its name from the province of Perm, in the Ural Mountain region of eastern Russia, where the rocks of the youngest division of the Carboniferous system were first studied by Murchison, an English geologist, and named in honor of that province.

Late in Carboniferous time, probably at the beginning of the Permian epoch, some condition arose that caused world-wide changes. In some parts of the world mountains were formed, but in the Canyon country the land was raised but little out of the sea and was not greatly disturbed.

Thick beds of sand accumulated on the low-lying area. In some places these accumulations attained a thickness of more than a thousand feet. Then the sea returned and covered the sand with limy ooze. In time these deposits hardened into the rock formations known to geologists as the Coconino sandstone and the Kaibab limestone. These are the rocks of the precipitous cliffs at the rim of the canyon. In other parts of the plateau country the rocks of this age have a different aspect.

Probably the most notable scenic objects formed by the sandstones of Permian age are the natural bridges in eastern Utah. As these are among the most remarkable of known bridges, let us take a side trip and see them before we consider the landscapes of Permian time.

Natural Bridges

The natural bridges in White Canyon, Utah, first made known to the general public in 1904, were proclaimed a national monument in 1908. In this monument there are three bridges of great size and beauty. The largest is called Augusta by some and Sipapu (portal of life) by others; the smallest is the Edwin or Owanchomo (rock mound) (Plate XVII); and the third is called Caroline or Kachina (guardian spirit). The Indian name was suggested by a symbol carved on the bridge and recognized as that of the Kachina, the sacred dancers of the Hopi Indians.

These great bridges consist of white sandstone of Carboniferous age and were formed by erosion when White Canyon and its tributary, Armstrong Canyon, were cut. The smallest, and probably the oldest of the group, was formed in Armstrong Canyon about 3 miles above its junction with White Canyon. Here a narrow ridge was left between Armstrong Creek and an unnamed tributary. The two streams undercut this dividing ridge from opposite sides until they met under the upper part of the ridge, which was left as a bridge. The larger stream captured the smaller, leading the captive underneath the newly formed arch. Since the time of this stream piracy each channel has been cut far below the level of the ancient stream bed. The beam of rock which now bridges the captured stream is slowly weathering away but is still 10 feet thick and 35 feet wide in its narrowest part. It spans the unnamed valley 108 feet above the stream bed, the slender, graceful strip of rock being supported by abutments 194 feet apart. The dimensions here used for these bridges are those furnished by the National Park Service.

The Caroline bridge (Plate XVIII) was formed in a somewhat different manner. Long ago the stream that cut White Canyon at its junction with Armstrong Canyon flowed in a sinuous or meandering course, which it maintained as it cut downward into the white sandstone and thus formed what is known technically as an intrenched meander. Here it made a horseshoe-shaped gorge around a peninsula or mass of rock that is connected with the main wall by a narrow neck. As erosion proceeded the stream in White Canyon impinged against the rocks of this neck and undercut them. From the opposite side the same stream, aided by Armstrong Creek, which joins White Creek at this point, undercut the neck until a hole was formed through which White Creek took a short cut, abandoning the longer course around the peninsula. The upper part of the neck now forms Caroline bridge.

Caroline bridge is the youngest and most massive of the White Canyon group of bridges. It is rough-hewn, having the appearance of vigorous youth and giving the impression of great strength and endurance. Huge blocks of rock fallen from the walls suggest that the master workman was interrupted before his task was finished. Great masses of rocks, weighing tons, still hang to the wall from which nature chiseled them.

According to the National Park Service, Caroline bridge stands 205 feet above the bed of the stream it spans, and it springs from abutments 186 feet apart. The arch is reported to be 49 feet wide and to have a minimum thickness of 107 feet.

Augusta bridge (Plate XIX) stands in White Canyon 2½ miles above its junction with Armstrong Canyon. It is an enormous arch of white sandstone, whose abutments stand 261 feet apart. The great stone beam, 65 feet thick and 128 feet wide in its smallest part, spans the stream at a height of 222 feet above the water.

This wonderful piece of nature's handiwork, so perfectly carved and so symmetrically proportioned that it is difficult to realize its size, is set in the midst of a group of impressive rock forms. The canyon walls, which are formed of barren white sandstone, are high, steep, and rugged, and rise sheer from the narrow bed of the creek. In almost inaccessible nooks high in these walls may be seen cliff dwellings. Some of these dwellings, reminders of the ancient race of human beings which once flourished here but finally vanished, have never since been entered. The charm of mystery still lingers about them.

The modern Indians, who are supposed to be the descendants of the cliff dwellers, believe that they come into the world from a lower region through an opening which the Hopis call *Sipapu* — the door of life. After death they return through the same hole to the nether region, there to dwell for a time before mounting to the sky to become "rain-gods."

These bridges are far from ordinary routes of travel, and few people have seen them. One result of this isolation is their unmolested, clean appearance. The walls have not been marred by initials carved in the stone, nor have messages of the zealot or the advertiser been painted or smoked on the smooth faces of the rock. Some who have visited places of interest that were popular long ago and have seen the thousands of names and dates that disfigure the walls experience a thrill of delight as they read the notice posted at the camping place under Caroline bridge, which states in no uncertain words that name scratching is positively forbidden.

These natural bridges are the result of normal stream erosion in an elevated region. There is no mystery about them. Doubtless thousands of similar bridges have been formed and destroyed in ages past and other thousands will be made and later destroyed in ages to come.

The great sandstone of which they are made was formed long ago near sea level and was later covered by other beds of sediment many thousands of feet thick. Some of these rocks were formed by deposition in the sea after the white sandstone had been depressed far below sea level.

After being buried for uncounted eons, this sandstone, in common with other rocks of the plateau region, was raised and its elevated surface was exposed to erosion. Then, as now, the rain formed rills and the water of the rills gathered into rivulets and finally into rivers. These sought the lowest places on the surface in their way to the sea, just as they do at the present time.

Probably the elevation was slow and the rate of rise of the surface differed from place to place. Where the rise was slow enough broad, shallow valleys were eroded. Where the rise was relatively rapid deep, narrow canyons were cut. Also where the streams were flowing over soft rocks they tended to form broad valleys, and where they were flowing over hard rocks they tended to form narrow valleys.

Furthermore, the rate of elevation of the rocks varied from time to time. During a time of slow upward movement, or even of cessation of such movement, the streams tended to broaden their valleys and to meander widely over the evenly graded bottom lands.

These principles may be applied in picturing the formation of White Canyon. As the surface rose higher and higher the waters of the higher lands formed streams. These streams cut their channels deeper and eroded away the rocks at their sides, just as the streams do now. During the long ages in which this elevation and erosion were going on a thickness of thousands of feet of rock was removed from the plateau region.

In the course of its down-cutting the little stream which carved White Canyon meandered widely, carrying away the soft material of the red rocks that once covered the white sandstone. But when in its downward course it reached this hard sandstone it found erosion more difficult. But its meandering course was established and it cut its trench into the sandstone along this course. It continued its lateral cutting but made little headway toward broadening its canyon in the hard rock. Thus were formed the intrenched meanders, such as those at Caroline and Augusta bridges.

At Augusta bridge and at Caroline bridge the stream in its meandering course formed a loop resembling an ox-bow, flowing about a peninsula of rock that had a narrow neck. This neck was at the point where the stream was obliged to turn sharply in order to flow around the end of the peninsula. Also, on its return to the other side of the neck, it made a sharp turn in the opposite direction. It is the law of streams that they cut their banks on the outer side of curves. Thus the neck of the peninsula was undermined by the floods that surged against it from both sides. In time they broke through the neck and took the short cut through the hole thus formed. The end of the peninsula was left as an island, and the upper part of the neck remains as a bridge binding this island to the mainland.

Permian Landscapes

Returning now from our side trip, we may bring to an end our consideration of the Carboniferous period by mentioning the outstanding characteristic of this closing epoch of Carboniferous time. In order to picture the Permian landscape we must go far afield, for the rocks of Permian age are known more intimately in other parts of the world than in America.

The equable climate of Coal Measures time, which was so mild the world over that the epoch may be called one of universal summer, was changed in a most remarkable manner. The Permian epoch, which followed, seems to have been one of almost universal winter, for glaciers formed in some places practically at the equator. The material left by glacial ice in Permian time is found in India, Australia, Africa, Brazil, Canada, and other countries.

The change from low, swampy lands having a uniform, warm climate to a mountainous country having a cold, variable climate caused corresponding changes in the plants and animals. The changes, however, were not sudden. They extended over a period of time measured probably in hundreds of thousands or perhaps millions of years. Two conspicuous results were the development of cold-climate plants and of highly organized reptiles.

The Permian reptiles in all parts of the world seem to have had unusually strange characteristics. One of the lizard-like creatures from Brazil had a tail as long as its body proper, with a notable enlargement in the middle of it. The Permian reptiles whose remains are found in South Africa were large, clumsy creatures with bones so massive and so curiously shaped that they have been called "reptilian bone-piles." But probably the most peculiar creature of all is the finback lizard, shown in Plate XXI, B, whose remains are found in Texas. The so-called fin was produced by elongated spines half as long as the body. Many varieties of these strange creatures have been found, ranging in length from 3 to 10 feet.

Chapter V

TRIASSIC SCENES

The rocks of middle age — of the Mesozoic era — (see table of geologic time on page 59) are widely distributed through western America. In general they are softer than the older rocks and have been eroded away near the Grand Canyon. However, they are conspicuous where they have escaped the vigorous erosion of Colorado River and its tributary streams.

The middle age is subdivided into the Triassic, Jurassic, and Cretaceous periods. The first of these will be illustrated by the Petrified Forest National Monument, in Arizona; the second by Zion National Park, in Utah; and the last by Mesa Verde National Park, in Colorado.

The rocks of Triassic age in the high plateaus of western America consist chiefly of red shale and sandstone. They form two groups, the lower or older group containing shells of marine mollusks, and the upper or younger group containing fossil wood and the bones of land animals. These fossils show that the rocks of the lower group were formed when the sea covered parts of western America, and that those of the upper group were formed after this region had been raised above sea level.

The rocks of the lower group, known to geologists as the Moenkopi formation, are so conspicuously red that they have been called the painted rocks. In northern Arizona, near the Petrified Forest, these highly colored rocks are exposed to view as far as the eye can reach. This is a semi-desert region, where there is little grass on the ground under the best circumstances and scarcely a tuft where foraging sheep have passed.

The Painted Desert

Here we find small bunches of sagebrush and greasewood, which shelter jackrabbits and their enemies, the wildcats; and in places bunches of ground cactus, near which may be seen large and brilliantly colored lizards, as well as small, dull-colored ones, which dart here and there with incredible swiftness. Also here may be seen the clumsy little horned toads that are found in so many places on the western plains.

A few larger plants, such as the yucca, commonly called soapweed, which consists of a bristling mass of bayonets, grow here. Occasionally a desert sparrow may be seen, or one of the little owls that live in burrows deserted by prairie dogs. One who is especially fortunate may sometimes see in the distance a predatory coyote.

But the principal features that attract the traveler's attention are the barren surface, the highly colored rocks, and the peculiar forms of erosion which characterize the Painted Desert. There is too little rainfall here to wash the road, but the vagrant winds keep it clear of dust in some places and pile up heaps of sand in others. From this naturally paved highway the traveler views the gorgeous landscape. He has the joy of a wide horizon, the bluest of blue skies, and clear, bracing air. No tree shuts off his view, and he can see no human habitation as far as his eye can reach — just colored rocks and sand and cactus and blue sky.

The Painted Desert presents varied and highly colored landscapes. There are badland forms, rounded domes, oval ridges, and trenchlike valleys of intricate pattern. Where some layers of the rock are harder than the others there are mesas, buttes, towers, and monuments. Leading up to the mesas are steps, with hard rocks forming the treads and soft rocks the risers. There are bands of yellow, gray, drab, lavender, pink, lilac, and brown in numerous shades. There are patches of blue and green and white, and even of black. There is every conceivable combination of colors.

The upper group of Triassic rocks, known to geologists as the Chinle formation, is scarcely less brilliant than the lower group, but its crowning glory lies in the petrified wood which it contains, best seen in the well-known Petrified Forest of Arizona.

Some readers will associate this forest with Holbrook, others with Adamana, the station at which they left the train to view the stone trees.

The name Adamana recalls Adam Hanna, one of the pioneers of the West, a rough-and-ready character quite able to take care of himself in a lawless country — and for that matter to take care of some of the lawless members of the country, as his long record in the office of sheriff testifies. He was the first to entertain visitors to the Petrified Forest south of his ranch. An article published in 1889 records his complaint that only a dozen people that year saw the wonders which he stood ready to show them while 3,000 visited Yellowstone National Park. These figures are illuminating when compared with those for 1925, when more than 55,000 people visited the Petrified Forest and 154,000 entered Yellowstone Park.

Stone Trees and Wild Stories

The Petrified Forest is justly rated as one of the world's great wonders. Petrified wood is found at many other places in Arizona and elsewhere, but nowhere else are seen such enormous quantities of beautifully colored and perfectly preserved forms of great forest trees (Plate XXII). Many of the trunks are petrified in agate, chalcedony, and jasper; a few in rocks of the same age elsewhere are preserved in copper and iron. Some are turned partly to coal; in others some of the woody material was replaced by silver and by carnotite, a radium-bearing ore.

Some visitors, on entering the Petrified Forest, are much disappointed when they fail to find the stone trees standing upright. Guides can scarcely be blamed for repeating to credulous visitors the burlesques on stories told by irresponsible natives to tourists who are eager to hear strange tales as well as to see strange sights. A favorite yarn tells of "fossil trees in fossil leaf with fossil birds singing fossil songs in the petrified branches." Some even add that a fossil bird shot in mid-air by a fossil hunter did not fall because "even the force of gravity is petrified here." A source of enjoyment not appreciated by the joking guide is his use of the word, which he pronounces "peat-re-fied."

The petrified wood was first brought to the attention of white men by Lieutenant Whipple in 1853. One of the original transcontinental railway routes, the one now utilized by the Santa Fe system, was surveyed near the forest, and since the railroad was built the forest has become better known.

But although white men were slow in making the wonders of this region generally known, it was familiar to the aborigines for untold generations. Archeologists who have studied the records left by them believe that the region was the scene of four somewhat distinct civilizations, extending from the Pueblo Indians, who still inhabit the Southwest, back to the Aztecs. Something is known of two of these civilizations but very little of the other two. The records are of several kinds, including implements, potsherds, pictographs carved on smooth faces of rock, and ruined buildings.

Some of the prehistoric dwellings were made of petrified wood. Never were buildings, ancient or modern, more truly unique, and never were palaces built of more beautiful material, for these prehistoric homes were made of great brilliant gems of jasper, chalcedony, and agate. The prehistoric men selected their building material from the remains of still older prehistoric trees, for just as the Aztecs belong to a race now dead, these stone trees belong to a vegetable world which has left no living species.

These ruined Indian houses, built of selected pieces of fossil logs, cemented together with clay, gave rise a few years ago to an unfounded story that the dwellings of a prehistoric race had been constructed of trees then living, and that the ruins are "petrified log houses."

Ancient and Modern Uses of Petrified Wood

But the prehistoric use of the petrified wood did not cease with the building of dwellings. From it were manufactured arrow heads and knives and stone hammers. These implements found their way through the narrow channels of Aztec commerce over hundreds of miles. This commerce was checked by the extinction of the race.

The modern traffic in petrified wood, which for a time threatened to destroy the natural aspect of the Petrified Forest, was happily checked in a better way, when the tract of land containing the best of the stone trees was set aside as a national monument. Before the commercialism was checked many carloads of the material were shipped away and cut into ornaments, and machinery had been sent to Adamana for the purpose of crushing the fossil trees into abrasive material for the manufacture of sandpaper. Fortunately the machinery was never operated for this purpose.

To one entering the forest a strange and at first puzzling scene presents itself. The fragments of petrified wood cover the surface of the ground in great profusion. There are myriads of small pieces or chips, and in some places, especially in the hollows, the ground is literally paved with cross sections of the stone logs resembling blocks of stove-wood. Only easily gullible persons will listen to statements that these so-called chips result from the activities of prehistoric men wielding their stone axes. The "chips" are simply fragments of petrified wood broken from the logs on their exposure to the air, chiefly by expansion and contraction under the influence of heat and frost. The sections range in length from several feet down to an inch or two. Some of them are so related to one another that they were obviously derived from the same log, but most of them lie in disorder so great that the forest may appropriately be called ruins. At few places are logs seen in the rocks.

Where did all the petrified wood seen at the surface come from?

This question is answered when we go to the forest, where a natural bridge is formed by an unbroken fossil log. This log is 4 feet in diameter at the base and 18 inches in diameter at the top, and is 111 feet long. It now spans a ravine 30 feet wide and 20 feet deep. At both ends the log is embedded in the rock in which it was originally buried. In technical language this petrified tree is "in place." Others may be found in place in the same rocks near the tops of the mesas.

If this great log were not artificially supported a time would soon come when the walls of the widening gulch would no longer support it and it would fall, probably breaking into large segments. These would lie on the floor of the valley until the stream undermined them again and would then fall or roll to a new and lower position. As this process was repeated again and again the segments would be scattered more and more widely.

In a similar manner were formed the valleys just mentioned and the disordered accumulations of petrified wood. The fragments, some of which now lie in jumbled masses, once formed logs similar to that of the bridge and were embedded in rocks which once extended across the site of the present valleys.

These rocks disintegrated and were slowly washed away to form the valleys, in much the same way that the intermittent stream is now washing away the rock under the bridge. The petrified logs have thus been let down, some of them several hundred feet, and the petrified wood now on the ground represents logs that were originally distributed through a considerable thickness of rock.

Concerning the kind of trees and the manner in which their species are determined, Dr. F. H. Knowlton, of the United States National Museum, says:

> This process of silicification, and perhaps subsequent crystallization, was such that in some specimens the original form and texture of the wood cells has been greatly distorted or even destroyed entirely, while in others it is preserved so well that each cell, with its most intimate structural details, is retained with astonishing fidelity. Thin sections of this wood [ground until they are about 0.003 of an inch thick] may therefore be studied under the microscope with almost as much satisfaction as thin sections cut from a living tree. Although a complete microscopical examination has not yet been made of all these woods of the region, all from the area south of the railroad that have been examined prove to belong to a single species which has been described by the writer under the name *Araucarioxylon arizonicum.* That is, it is simply the wood of an ancient *Araucaria*, which, it is well known, does not now live in the northern hemisphere. In this wood the annual or growth rings are not apparent to the naked eye, but under the microscope they are observed to be present, though rather poorly developed and somewhat obscure, the yearly growths being separated by a layer of 2–5 tangentially compressed cells. In radial section the tracheids are observed to be provided with numerous bordered pits, which are disposed in a single contiguous row, or occasionally in two mutually compressed rows. The medullary rays, as seen in this section, are composed of short, thin-walled cells which, in at least some specimens, are provided with small oval pores. In tangential section the rays are found to be in a single vertical series of from 1 to 22 cells.

Several species of trees are present in the fossil forests, as may readily be seen on examining the microscopic sections, but the only other species that has been described comes from the "north" forest, the small forest north of the railroad. It is quite different from the other species, and while undoubtedly araucarian in character, shows so many points of divergence from the living *Araucaria* that Dr. E. C. Jeffrey, of Harvard University, by whom it was studied, created for it a new genus. It is known as *Woodworthia arizonica.* It is remarkable in that it was provided with short shoots which persisted in the wood of the trunk throughout the life of the tree and now show as pits or scars on the surface. It probably was the presence of twin scars, one on either side of and a little below the principal scar, thus suggesting the lateral cicatricules of the leaf scar of one of the great Paleozoic lycopods, *Sigillaria,* that led Mr. John Muir to name this forest the "Sigillaria" forest. This name was shown to be entirely erroneous and inapplicable by David White, who reports that no *Sigillaria* or *Lepidodendron* are present in these forests.

Fanciful Accounts

The intense interest in these ancient trees, some of which must have been nearly 10 feet in diameter and more than 200 feet high, has led to many a flight of fancy[1] and to many an inference which is either wholly erroneous or is so expressed as to give a wrong impression. On the other hand, interest in the petrified trees has led to published accounts which contain valuable information. Probably the questions most often asked

[1] From a folder given out for the "information" of tourists I quote the following, with bracketed comments of my own:

"What human interest attaches to every foot of the ground! What race of men knew the living forest! [It was destroyed millions of years before men existed.] What birds sang in its swaying boughs! [Birds had not yet come into existence.] What creatures browsed beneath its protecting arms! What shock of earth [the shock is ours] brought low these monarchs, stately pine and giant oak! [There were stately pines but no giant oaks. No oak trees of any kind lived then.] Were they petrified where they fell or did they float out on the tide of a forgotten sea? [Neither. The rocks containing the logs are non-marine and their physical characteristics indicate that they were deposited by streams and that the logs floated down rivers and were buried in their sands.]

are, How did the logs get to their present position, and why did they turn to stone?

How Wood Turns to Stone

The details of the process by which wood is replaced with silica or other mineral substances are not well understood. In some way the woody substance is removed and its place is taken by mineral matter in such a way that the cellular structure and even the most minute features of the wood are preserved. A piece of agatized wood does not seem readily soluble, yet the agate was all deposited from solution. Silica is slightly soluble in water containing soda and potash. Probably the logs, after being deeply buried by sand and mud, in which they were entombed for millions of years, were permeated by alkaline waters bearing silica in solution, and as the wood decayed it was replaced particle by particle with silica. The brilliant hues are caused by small amounts of iron and manganese, which color the silica — a natural process reproduced artificially in making stained glass. On exposure to the air the logs become still more highly colored by the further oxidation of the metallic coloring material. The logs at the surface are more brilliantly colored than those only recently exposed.

The occurrence of the logs in their present position calls for further explanation. They all lie prostrate. Their ends were battered and their sides were bruised. From most of them the bark was stripped before they were buried. Very few have roots or branches attached. In some places the logs lie in a tangled mass resembling a log jam.

A few stumps have been found. Some of these, now turned to stone, seem to have been buried where they stood rooted in the ancient soil. But at least one stump was found inverted, with roots uppermost. It had been overturned and possibly had floated for a long distance before it was buried in the sand.

The rocks that inclose the logs contain the shells of fresh-water mollusks and the bones of ancient crocodiles and other animals supposed to have lived in streams and in marshy places. Some of the slabs of rocks bear ripple marks formed either by shallow water when the beds of mud were soft or by wind when the sand was dry. Sun-cracks and rain-prints are also found, which tell as plainly as printed words could tell of the exposure of the soft material to the storms and the sunshine of that ancient time.

These facts and many others have been considered in working out the story of the plateau country at the time the logs of the Petrified Forest were entombed, and the changes that occurred during this long period. The story thus worked out by the geologist may be told briefly as follows.

Changes in Sea and Land

When the Southwest emerged from the sea in which the limestone (Kaibab) seen at the rim of Grand Canyon was formed, the rocks were exposed to erosion for a time but were again covered by sea water, which came from the Pacific Ocean, probably across California, Nevada, and Utah. This invasion by the sea took place long before the mountains of California were born. The rocks formed in this sea — the Moenkopi formation — contain beds of salt and gypsum, which were deposited in land-locked bays. In a well drilled at Adamana, salt water was found in this formation.

Apparently the land in northern Arizona was rising during Moenkopi time, and by the end of that epoch the sea water had been expelled. Then followed a long period of exposure to subaërial erosion, represented by a break or unconformity between the Moenkopi formation and the overlying beds, the lowest of which is called the Shinarump conglomerate. This period of erosion lasted so long that a large part of the plateau country was worn down by rain and stream to a nearly level plain.

Then, for some reason not definitely known, the streams that had planed the country to a general level became unable to carry their load of sand and pebbles. The material dropped by the weakened currents choked the channels and diverted the streams to new courses, where the process was repeated. Thus the Shinarump conglomerate was formed.

Just as happens now during times of flood, some of the trees that grew on the uplands were washed into the rivers, floated downstream, and after long buffeting and grinding were deposited on some shoal, where they became waterlogged and were finally covered with mud and sand.

Weapons of the Wolf God

In the Piute mythology the broken trunks of the stone trees are the weapons of Shinau′ äv, the great Wolf God. (In some accounts spelled Shinarav.) The accumulated masses, such as those in the Petrified Forest, are said to mark the battlefields of this warrior god. The presence of petrified wood suggested to Major Powell the appropriateness of the name Shinarump (the weapons of Shinau′ äv) for the rocks containing them. This name has since been restricted to the conglomerate, and another name, Chinle, has been applied to the overlying rocks. Prof. H. E. Gregory adds that, to the Navajo Indians the petrified logs are yeitsobitsin, the bones of Yeitso, a monster who was destroyed by the Indians' sun god and whose congealed blood forms the lava flows of the region.

As the plain was built up layer on layer, only the finer material could be handled by the streams. Hence the later deposits — the Chinle formation — contain pebbles in relatively few places. But the decrease in the carrying power of the streams, which prevented them from transporting pebbles, did not affect their ability to carry the floating timber. Hence the logs are found from the bottom to the top of this formation.

Triassic Animals and Plants

The process of building up the plain continued until a thickness of more than a thousand feet of material had accumulated. Where did it all come from and where did the trees grow which were washed out upon the plain?

It is supposed that the sea of early Triassic time was an arm of the Pacific Ocean, which washed the base of the ancient highlands, some of which stood approximately where the Rocky Mountains of Colorado now stand. The giant pines now preserved as stone logs may have grown on the western slopes of the ancient Rockies, as their descendants, the giant sequoias, are growing now in California on the western slope of the Sierra Nevada.

The age of reptiles begins with the Triassic period, although recent discoveries show that reptiles probably originated in the preceding period. The Triassic was a time when reptilian life dominated earth, sea, and air. Land reptiles, swimming reptiles, and flying dragons all lived in Triassic time. Although they did not reach the climax of their development until the following age, the principal types of reptiles lived in Triassic time.

Probably the most notable of these reptiles are the dinosaurs, a name meaning terrible saurians. They constituted the reigning dynasty of the Mesozoic era. Some of these ungainly creatures walked upright and had three-toed feet which made tracks like those of a bird. As birds had not yet developed the famous "bird tracks" of this age were probably made by three-toed dinosaurs.

Some of the reptilian horde became swimmers, such as the

sea turtles, the ichthyosaurs, and the plesiosaurs; others developed batlike wings and took possession of the air.

The processes of elimination of the old spore-bearing plants of Carboniferous time and the development of the modern seed bearers, which progressed so rapidly in Permian time, were continued in the Triassic. None of the trees which grew so luxuriantly in Coal Measures time have been found in rocks of Triassic age, although the ferns and rushes continued to thrive. Many species of Triassic cycads are known. These plants, now almost extinct, were so abundant in the Triassic and next younger period that the Mesozoic is sometimes called the Age of Cycads.

But the plants that attract most attention, because of their conspicuous fossil remains found in the Petrified Forest, are the giant pines that grew in southwestern America. These pines lived also in the central and eastern parts of the United States, together with other cone-bearing trees, tree ferns, cycads, and gigantic horsetails. From the fossil pines we get some idea of climate, for they possess rings of growth that indicate growing seasons alternating with periods of rest and therefore change of season.

One of the most interesting of the Triassic plants is the *Ginkgo*, the maidenhair tree. It has a wonderful history, perhaps a more remarkable history than any other tree now living. It has come to us practically unchanged from earliest Mesozoic time. Apparently it reached its widest distribution in the Jurassic period, when it spread over much of the globe. Since Jurassic time it has been gradually diminishing, until at present it is represented by a single living species, native to Japan and China.

In the far East the Ginkgo is regarded as a sacred tree and as such is planted about the temples and sanctuaries. Possibly it has been preserved in this way, for it is not known anywhere

Plate XVII. Edwin Bridge, the Oldest and Most Graceful of the Natural Bridges in Bridges National Monument, Utah.

A remnant of white sandstone left by stream erosion and shaped by weathering. Photograph by Willis T. Lee.

Plate XVIII. Caroline Bridge, the Youngest and Most Massive of the Natural Bridges in Bridges National Monument, Utah.

Photograph by Willis T. Lee.

at the present time in a truly wild state. It does not seem likely to become extinct as long as civilized men prize its fascinating history and admire its curious foliage. It is a familiar sight on the streets of Washington, D.C., and is cultivated in many parts of the world.

Close of Triassic Time

As the greater part of North America was above water and undergoing erosion during most of the Triassic period, sedimentary records were then being destroyed over most of the continent. Because of this general destruction of evidence, little can be said definitely of the geologic events that brought the Triassic period to a close. At or near the end of the period great crustal disturbances occurred in many parts of the earth, which resulted in the formation of mountains, in a change of level of broad areas of land, and in the shifting of seas. Just when and how these disturbances occurred may be left to the professional geologist, but their influence on western America is of general interest, for it was this new continent that furnished the material for the Jurassic rocks, which make the most remarkable landscapes of the plateau country.

CHAPTER VI

JURASSIC SCENES

THE second period of the Mesozoic era, or middle age, is called Jurassic, a name taken from the Jura Mountains, in Europe, where these rocks were studied. During this period were formed the rocks which make the Plateau country the natural picture gallery of the world. These rocks are perhaps best exhibited in Zion National Park, in southern Utah.

Zion National Park

Zion Canyon is almost unique among natural wonders. It is a narrow gorge cut in highly colored rock between nearly vertical walls about 3,000 feet high (Plate XXIII).

Canyons form a group of scenic landscapes that are second in impressiveness only to those formed by mountains. Grand Canyon is the most impressive of the group, and Zion Canyon is one of its tributaries. Of all the stream-cut gorges, Zion Canyon is one of the most conspicuous. Niagara Gorge seems impressive as we gaze into its depths, but fifteen Niagaras might be placed in Zion Canyon, one above the other, before they reached the rim. The splendidly colored rocks carved by natural forces in impressive outlines; the great walls rising in astonishing grandeur; the deep, narrow trench cut by the little stream working through untold ages — they cannot be described, they must be seen.

Zion Canyon is in the southeastern part of the high plateaus of Utah and is notable for many features of unusual geologic and geographic interest. It also has archeologic interest, for

FIGURE 2.—Temples of the Virgin, Zion Canyon

Upper figure, the Western Temple; lower figure, the Eastern Temple

here are found the remains of prehistoric races of America and of ancestral Indian tribes. Its geologic features include craters of extinct volcanoes, fossiliferous deposits, and brilliantly colored strata, among which are some that are believed to be the best representations in the world of a rare type of sedimentation. The features of geographic interest include a labyrinth of remarkable canyons that have highly ornate and beautifully colored walls.

The principal canyon in Zion National Park is occupied by the North Fork of Virgin River. It is called Mukuntuweap by some, and Zion Canyon by others. The name Zion Canyon is employed much more frequently than Mukuntuweap, and it was in use among the settlers of Utah for several years before Major J. W. Powell described the canyon under the Indian name.

The rocks that we saw in the Petrified Forest appear also in Zion Canyon, but here they are overlain by a massive red sandstone, which is one of the dominating features in the marvelous scenery of the plateau country. This sandstone (Plate XXIV) is more than 2,000 feet thick and is brilliantly colored from top to bottom. It has been called the Vermilion Cliff sandstone because it forms Vermilion Cliffs, east of this canyon. It is overlain by a white sandstone about 1,000 feet thick, the two sandstones together forming walls that rise almost vertically to heights of more than half a mile.

Temples of the Virgin

Among the conspicuous objects of interest in Zion Canyon are two enormous natural structures that have been called the Temples of the Virgin (Figure 2). These consist of the richly red Vermilion Cliff sandstone below and the White Cliff sandstone above. Some idea of the magnitude and glory of these structures is conveyed by the name temples.

PLATE XIX. AUGUSTA BRIDGE, KNOWN ALSO AS SIPAPU (GATE OF HEAVEN).

This is the largest bridge in Bridges National Monument, Utah. It is said to have the following dimensions: span, 261 feet; height of arch, 222 feet; thickness in center, 65 feet; width in center, 128 feet. For scale, note the man on the bridge. Photograph by Willis T. Lee.

Plate XX. View in Monument Valley, a Possible National Park, Showing Some of the Enormous Monuments of Red Sandstone for Which the Park Is Famous.

Photograph by Willis T. Lee.

It was the western Temple that served as a landmark to guide Major Powell and his party across the desert from the mouth of Virgin River to Salt Lake City after they had completed their remarkable exploration of Grand Canyon. His account seems to show that the spires of the Temple were recognized from a distance of 60 or 70 miles.

The eastern Temple of the Virgin is as imposing as the western Temple and in some respects more fascinating, but it does not appear to as good advantage from the entrance to the canyon.

These temples have justly been regarded as preëminent among forms of natural architecture. In comparing them with the noble and wonderfully ornate buttes — the so-called temples — in the Grand Canyon, Major Clarence Dutton, an early authority on the plateau region, acknowledged that for "nobility of form, beauty of decoration, and splendor of color, the Temples of the Virgin must . . . be awarded the palm."

The temples are great remnants of an old plateau — that is, they are parts of it that have not been worn down. The beds of rock of which they are formed were once connected across the canyon that now separates them and extended far to the south and west over a wide area. Their original extent will probably never be known, for with the elevation of the plateau region they were in large part eroded and carried away, and it is their remnants that now form the glorious scenery of Zion Canyon.

In his description of the Vermilion Cliffs near Zion Canyon, Major Dutton advises that "We must be frugal of adjectives lest . . . we find their force and meaning exhausted," and he truthfully states that the ornate sculpture and the rich coloring of the cliff walls "might justify very exalted language of description." He says:

Vermilion Cliffs

There are portions of the Vermilion Cliffs which in some respects lay hold of the sensibilities with a force not much less overwhelming than the majesty of the Grand Canyon; not in the same way, not by virtue of the same elements of power and impressiveness, but in a way of their own and by attributes of their own. In mass and grandeur and in the extent of the display there is no comparison; it would be like comparing a private picture gallery containing a few priceless treasures with the wealth of art in the Vatican or Louvre.

The profile of the Vermilion Cliffs is very complex, though conforming to a definite type and made up of simple elements. Though it varies much in different localities it never loses its typical character. It consists of a series of vertical ledges rising tier above tier, story above story, with intervening slopes covered with talus, through which the beds project their fretted edges. The stratification is always revealed with perfect distinctness and is even emphasized by the peculiar weathering. . . . Where the profiles are thrown well into view the vertical lines, which bound the faces of the ledges, are quite perpendicular and straight, while the lines of the intervening slopes are feebly concave. . . . This effect is much enhanced by the manner in which the wall advances in promontories or recedes in alcoves, and by the wings and gables with sharp corners and Mansard roofs jutting out from every lateral face where there is the least danger of blankness or monotony. . . . This sandstone has many strong features and yet they elude description. One point, however, may be seized upon, and that is a series of nearly vertical joints with which the mass is everywhere riven. The fissures thus produced have been slowly enlarged by weathering, and down the face of every escarpment run the dark shadows of these rifts. They reach often from top to bottom of the mass and penetrate deeply its recesses. Wherever this great member forms the entablature — and west of Pipe Spring it usually does so — its crest is uneven and presents towers and buttresses produced by the widening of these cracks. Near Short Creek [about 10 miles southeast of Rockville] it breaks into lofty truncated towers of great beauty and grandeur, with strongly emphasized vertical lines and decorations suggestive of cathedral architecture on a colossal scale. Still loftier and more ornate become the structures as we approach the Virgin. At length they reach the sublime. The altitudes increase until they approach 2000 feet above the plain. The wall is recessed with large amphitheatres, buttressed with huge spurs, and decorated with towers and pinnacles. Here, too, for the first time along their westward trend the Vermilion Cliffs send off buttes. And giant buttes they verily are, rearing their unassailable summits into the domain of the clouds, rich with the aspiring forms of Gothic type, and flinging back in red and purple the intense sunlight poured over them. Could the imagination blanch these colors, it might compare them with vast icebergs, rent from the front of a glacier and floating majestically out to sea, only here it is the parent mass that recedes, melting away through the ages, while its offspring stands still; yet the analogy would be a feeble one, for the buttes are grander, more definite in form, and many times loftier. But the climax of this scenery is still beyond.

Late in the autumn of 1880 I rode along the base of Vermilion Cliff from Kanab to the Virgin, having the esteemed companionship of Mr. Holmes. We had spent the summer and most of the autumn among the cones of the Uinkaret, in the dreamy parks and forests of the Kaibab, and in the solitudes of the intervening desert; and our sensibilities had been somewhat overtasked by the scenery of the Grand Canyon. It seemed to us that all grandeur and beauty thereafter beheld must be mentally projected against the recollection of those scenes, and be dwarfed into commonplace by the comparison; but as we moved onward the walls increased in altitude, in animation, and in power. At length the towers of Short Creek burst into view, and, beyond, the great cliff in long perspective thrusting out into the desert plain its gables and spurs. . . .

As we moved northward from Short Creek we had frequent opportunities to admire these cliffs and buttes, with the conviction that they were revealed to us in their real magnitudes and in their true relations. They awakened an enthusiasm more vivid than we had anticipated, and one which the recollection of far grander scenes did not dispel. At length the trail descended into a shallow basin, where a low ledge of sandstone, immediately upon the right, shut them out from view; but as we mounted the opposite rim a new scene, grander and more beautiful than before, suddenly broke upon us.

The cliff again appeared, presenting the heavy sandstone member in a sheer wall nearly a thousand feet high, with a steep talus beneath it of eleven or twelve hundred feet more. Wide alcoves receded far back into the mass and in their depths the clouds floated. Long, sharp spurs plunged swiftly down, thrusting their monstrous buttresses into the plain below, and sending up pinnacles and towers along the knife edges. But the controlling object was a great butte which sprang into view immediately before us, and which the salient of the wall had hitherto masked. Upon a pedestal two miles long and 1,000 feet high, richly decorated with horizontal mouldings, rose four towers highly suggestive of cathedral architecture. Their altitude above the plain was estimated at about 1,800 feet. They were separated by vertical clefts made by the enlargement of the joints, and many smaller clefts extending from the summits to the pedestal carved the turrets into tapering buttresses, which gave a graceful, aspiring effect, with a remarkable definiteness, to the forms. We named it Smithsonian Butte, and it was decided that a sketch should be made of it; but in a few moments the plan was abandoned or forgotten, for over a notch or saddle formed by a low isthmus which connected the butte with the principal mesa there sailed slowly and majestically into view, as we rode along, a wonderful object. Deeply moved, we paused a moment to contemplate it, and then abandoning the trail we rode rapidly toward the notch, beyond which it soon sank out of sight. In an hour's time we reached the crest of the isthmus, and in an instant there flashed before us a scene never to be forgotten. In coming time it will, I believe, take rank with a very small number of spectacles each of which will, in its own way, be regarded as the most exquisite of its kind which the world discloses. The scene before us was The Temples and Towers of the Virgin.

At our feet the surface drops down by cliff and talus 1,200 feet upon a broad and rugged plain cut by narrow canyons. The slopes, the winding ledges, the bosses of projecting rock, the naked, scanty soil, display colors which are truly amazing. Chocolate, maroon, purple, lavender, magenta, with broad bands of toned white, are laid in horizontal belts, strongly contrasting with each other, and the ever-varying slope of the surface cuts across them capriciously, so that the sharply defined belts wind about like the contours of a map. From right to left across the further foreground of the picture stretches the inner canyon of the Virgin, about 700 feet in depth and here of considerable width. Its bottom is for the most part unseen, but in one place is disclosed by a turn in its course, showing the vivid green of vegetation. Across the canyon, and rather more than a mile and a half beyond it, stands the central and commanding object of the picture, the western temple, rising 4,000 feet above the river. Its glorious summit was the object we had seen an hour before, and now the matchless beauty and majesty of its vast mass is all before us. Yet it is only the central object of a mighty throne of structures wrought up to the same exalted style and filling up the entire panorama. Right opposite us are the two principal forks of the Virgin, the Parunuweap coming from the right or east, and the Mukuntuweap or Little Zion Valley, descending towards us from the north. The Parunuweap is seen emerging on the extreme right through a stupendous gateway and chasm in the Triassic terrace, nearly 3,000 feet in depth. The further wall of this canyon, at the opening of the gateway, quickly swings northward at a right angle and becomes the eastern wall of Little Zion Valley. As it sweeps down the Parunuweap it breaks into great pediments, covered all over with the richest carving. The effect is much like that which the architect of the Milan Cathedral appears to have designed, though here it is vividly suggested rather than fully realized, as an artist painting in the "broad style" suggests many things without actually drawing them. The sumptuous, bewildering, mazy effect is all there, but when we attempt to analyze it in detail it eludes us. The flank of the wall receding up the Mukuntuweap is for a mile or two similarly decorated but soon breaks into new forms, much more impressive and wonderful. A row of towers half a mile high is quarried out of the palisade, and stands well advanced from its face. There is an eloquence to their forms which stirs the imagination with a singular power, and kindles in the mind of the dullest observer a glowing response. Just behind them, rising a thousand feet higher, is the eastern temple, crowned with a cylindric dome of white sandstone; but since it is, in many respects, a repetition of the nearer western temple, we may turn our attention to the latter. Directly in front of us a complex group of white towers, springing from a central pile, mounts upwards to the clouds. Out of their midst, and high over all, rises a dome-like mass, which dominates the entire landscape. It is almost pure white, with brilliant streaks of carmine descending its vertical walls. At the summit it is truncated, and a flat tablet is laid upon the top, showing its edge of deep red. It is impossible to liken this object to any familiar shape, for it resembles none. Yet its shape is far from being indefinite; on the contrary it has a definiteness and individuality which extort an exclamation of surprise when first beheld. There is no name provided for such an object, nor is it worth while to invent one. Call it a dome; not because it has the ordinary shape of such a structure, but because it performs the function of a dome. . . .

Nothing can exceed the wondrous beauty of Little Zion Valley, which separates the two temples and their respective groups of towers. Nor are these the only sublime structures which look down into its depths, for similar ones are seen on either hand along its receding vista until a turn in the course carries the valley out of sight. In its proportions it is about equal to Yosemite, but in the nobility and beauty of the sculptures there is no comparison.

Gates of Zion

On entering Zion Canyon we pass what have been called the Gates of Zion and three wonderful monuments, which some have called the Three Buttes and others the Three Patriarchs (Plate XXV). The region in which they stand was called Rock-Rovers Land by the Indians.

According to Major Powell, this was believed by the Indians to be the home of spirits called Tú-nu-ur-gwait′-si-gaip, or Rock-Rovers. It was said that these spirits once kindled a fire on one of the spires, the walls of which are so precipitous that no man can climb them. Although the Indians entered the canyon occasionally in pursuit of game, they could not be persuaded to spend the night there, for they believed that evil spirits lurked in the dark recesses to punish intruders.

On passing the Gates of Zion one enters an enormous trench whose walls rise almost vertically more than 3,000 feet. On the west is the Streaked Wall, so called because the face of the upper part of the cliff, formed by the White Cliff sandstone, is streaked here and there by wash leached from the highly colored rocks above (Plate XXIV). On the east is the Brown Wall, upon which stand three prominent pinnacles. These splendid monuments may be seen to best advantage early in the afternoon, when their west faces are lighted by the declining sun, but before the shadows have crept far from the eastern wall of the canyon.

Within the canyon are scenes too numerous to mention and too wonderful to express in words. The Great Organ is there, and the Sphinx, and the impressive mass called the Angels' Landing, and the still more magnificent pile called the Great White Throne (Plate XXIV); and last but by no means least, the Narrows, pictured in Plate XXIII.

The Narrows

Although the Narrows is a place visited by few people, it has been an object of wonder and admiration for many years, and many have gazed into it from a safe distance. In 1872 Doctor G. K. Gilbert entered Zion Canyon from the north through this narrow defile. From his account, published three years later, I quote as follows:

> The north fork . . . traverses, in the most wonderful defile it has been my fortune to behold, the massive sandstones of the Gray [White of other writers] and Vermilion Cliffs, here combined in a single undistinguishable body, certainly not less than 2,000 feet in depth. At the head of "The Narrows" the top of this bed is at the water's edge; and, as the strata rise and the stream descends southward, the height of the cañon-walls gradually increases until it includes the entire mass of sandstone. At the water's edge here the walls are perpendicular, but in the deeper parts they open out toward the top. As we entered and found our outlook of sky contracted — as we had never before seen it between cañon cliffs — I measured the aperture above, and found it 35°. We had thought

this a minimum, but soon discovered our error. Nearer and nearer the walls approached, and our strip of blue narrowed down to 20°, then 10°, and at last was even intercepted by the overhanging rocks. There was, perhaps, no point from which, neither forward nor backward, we could discover a patch of sky, but many times our upward view was completely cut off by the interlocking of the walls, which, remaining nearly parallel to each other, warped in and out as they ascended. For a number of miles the bottom of the cleft averages 30 feet in width, contracting frequently to 20, and in many places is entirely occupied by the stream, even at its low stage. Near the head of the cañon it is covered by sand and bowlders of sandstone, worn and fallen from the walls, and these continue throughout; but at a certain point a tributary gorge from the west brings in basaltic bowlders from some extinct volcano on the mesa above, and they abound to the end of the gorge. The superior toughness of the basalt enables it to withstand the shocks that rapidly crush the sandstone, and, though its supply must be far less, its rounded bowlders almost exclusively pave the river-bed for many miles. The course of the gorge is exceedingly tortuous, and, though our general direction in traversing it was southward, we yet journeyed toward all points of the compass in turn, our view in advance being usually limited at a few rods' distance by an angle. The side cañons all partake of the character of the main, but, being worn by smaller streams, are narrower, and their bottoms are of steeper grade. Many of them at their mouths are not cut so deep as the one we followed, and discharge at various heights above the river. . . . As a monument of denudation this chasm is an example — and a peculiarly differentiated example — of downward erosion by sand-bearing water. The principle on which the cutting depends is almost identical with that of the marble-saw, but the sand grains, instead of being imbedded in rigid iron, are carried by a flexible stream of water. By gravity they have been held against the bottom of the cut, so that they should make it vertical, but the current has carried them, in places, against one side or the other, and so far modified the influence of gravity that the cut undulates somewhat in its vertical section, as well as in its horizontal. The diagram represents an extreme but not exaggerated case of this departure from verticality, and, at the same time, shows the relation of the depth to the width of the cañon, where it is narrowest.

PLATE XXI, A. A CARBONIFEROUS LANDSCAPE.

Restoration of a forest of Coal Measures time, showing the great trunks of tree ferns and treelike club mosses.

PLATE XXI, B. MOUNTED SKELETON OF A PERMIAN REPTILE (DIMETRODON GIGAS).

Called Finback because of the long spines, which resemble those of the dorsal fin of a fish.

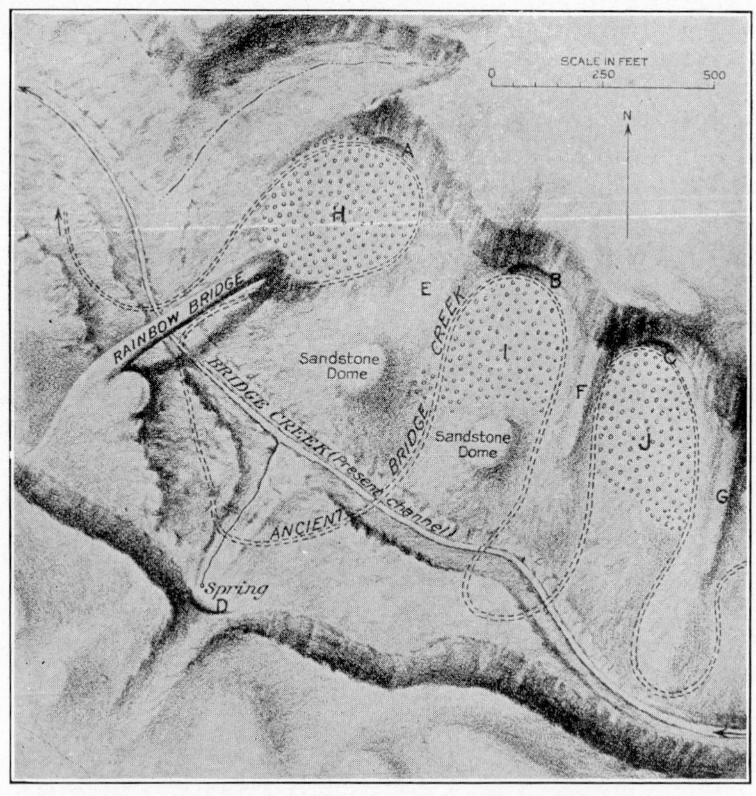

FIGURE 3.— DIAGRAMMATIC MAP OF RAINBOW BRIDGE, SHOWING THE COURSE AND THE DEPOSITS OF ANCIENT BRIDGE CREEK.

A, B, C, and D, notches and alcoves in canyon walls. Those at A, B, C, and possibly that at D, were cut by ancient Bridge Creek as it impinged against the canyon walls. E, F, and G, sandstone spurs that extended into loops of ancient Bridge Creek. H, I, and J, benches underlain by the deposits (represented by small circles) of ancient Bridge Creek. (Map drawn by C. A. Weckerly.)

The form at top is necessarily hypothetical; from our subterranean position we could form little idea of it.

Rainbow Bridge

Rainbow Bridge, called also Nonnezoshe (Plate XXVI), is a huge but graceful arch of sandstone, so high that it might span the dome of the National Capitol. This arch rises 309 feet above the bed of Bridge Creek and has a span of 278 feet. The sandstone at the top of the arch is 42 feet thick and 33 feet wide.

The bridge stands in a canyon so large that the great arch seems dwarfed. As Bridge Creek is a tributary of Colorado River, Rainbow Bridge belongs in the Grand Canyon group of natural wonders.

Here, as in many another place, one of the first questions asked is, What made it? According to H. D. Miser and others the bridge is a product of normal erosion. There is nothing supernormal about it. There are many similar natural bridges, but Rainbow Bridge commands special attention because of its large size.

The great arch was carved by the stream which now flows under it, in relatively recent time. To be sure, it has stood for untold ages as measured in terms of human life. But what is the lifetime of a man as compared with a geologic age? Bridge Canyon is young. The creek that formed it may have begun the work a million years ago — perhaps two millions: who can say? As it cut slowly downward, it swung from side to side wearing away the rocks, as illustrated in the accompanying diagrammatic map (Fig. 3).

Hills Only Relatively Everlasting

The rock spur at the bridge was undercut from both sides by the stream in its meandering course, as illustrated in Figure 3, until this stream broke through and took the shorter route underneath the newly formed arch.

As the stream continues to work during the coming ages, all vestiges of this great arch may be swept away and similar bridges may be formed in other places, just as scores of other arches were doubtless formed and swept away while Bridge Canyon was being cut.

But the observer should not hold the mistaken notion that natural wonders like the great stone arch are eternal. The "everlasting hills" are everlasting only in a relative sense. In comparison with human life they seem enduring. In comparison with the life of the earth their origin and destruction are mere incidents.

The white sandstone at the rim of Zion Canyon occurs widely throughout the plateau province and forms many of the scenic features of this province. In Rainbow Bridge National Monument, in southern Utah, it forms what is probably the most impressive natural bridge in the world.

This bridge was viewed by white men for the first time on August 14, 1909, when W. B. Douglas and others reached it under the guidance of two Piute Indians. In the following year the Rainbow Bridge National Monument was created by proclamation of President Taft.

Only a few of the living Indians knew of the existence of Rainbow Bridge prior to 1909, but it may have been an object of worship to the ancestors of these Indians. White Horse, a Navajo Indian who accompanied Mr. Douglas, refused, after passing under the bridge, to retrace his steps, because he had "evidently forgotten the prayer that the Navajos believe they are required to utter under penalty of death before they retrace their steps beneath an arch which to them represents the rainbow or sun path." White Horse therefore climbed laboriously around the end of the bridge rather than return by the easy path underneath it.

Story of the Jurassic Rocks

As the rocks of the Jurassic period — the middle period of the Mesozoic era — form so many of the scenic wonders of the West, it may be appropriate to sketch here the story of their origin. To understand this story we must reconstruct in imagination the geographic conditions during several successive periods of time and must envisage the progressive changes in the distribution of land and water and of deserts and swamps. We must realize that sea waves once rolled where great snow-capped peaks now stand, and that, in place of the sandy deserts of the present day, sluggish streams once meandered over broad, swampy lowlands.

The succession of events that are essential to this understanding begins with a time in the Carboniferous or Coal Measures period when the sea covered the region where the high plateaus and mountains now stand. This sea was expelled when the ancestors of the present Rocky Mountains rose east of the plateau region. For long ages these highlands withstood the elements, but they were finally torn down and swept away.

The débris from these mountains accumulated as the great beds of red sandstone and shale which make much of the gorgeous scenery in the foothills of the Rocky Mountains. The western base of these mountains was washed in early Triassic time by a sea which extended from the Pacific Ocean across the site of Grand Canyon.

This sea was finally filled and in its place was developed a broad, gently sloping plain, over which rivers meandered, bringing great tree trunks from the highlands and burying them in the sand and mud. Some of these may now be seen in the Petrified Forests of Arizona, already described.

Before the ancestral Rocky Mountains had entirely disappeared, other lands were elevated farther to the west, between them and the Pacific Ocean, and on these new lands mountains were thrown up. Probably these new mountains were high, for a desert was formed east of them, perhaps for the same reason that a desert now lies east of the High Sierra of California. The moisture from the Pacific was precipitated on these mountains and the streams carried a part of the rock waste eastward into the desert, where the winds reworked it, piling the sand into dunes which are now recognized in a fossil state in the rocks of Zion Canyon and other places.

In attempting to understand the geography of this region during the Jurassic period it is essential to realize that the conditions affecting the deposition of sediments in Triassic time were far different from those that prevailed in the Jurassic. The ancestral Rocky Mountains in Colorado, which had been highlands in Permian and Triassic time, were now worn down to rolling plains and low hills. It is equally important to realize that a desert exists only where the air contains little moisture. The present desert of western America is due in part to the high mountains near the Pacific Coast, which cool the moisture-laden winds and precipitate their moisture. In the same way the high mountains of the western continent of Jurassic time probably produced a desert, for the great mass of sandstone that makes some of the remarkable scenery of the canyon country originated as desert sand.

Jurassic Animals

However, this Jurassic desert was confined to western America. Other parts of the world teemed with animal life during the Jurassic period. The reptiles were highly developed and were the dominant creatures of the time. There were a few marsupials or mammals of the lowest types, which differed little from the reptiles. A few primitive mammals had existed in the Triassic period, but their development into the higher forms

Plate XXII. Petrified Forest, Arizona, Showing One of the Stone Logs Exposed by the Removal of the Rock in Which It Was Once Entombed.

The unbroken part of the log lies where it was buried in the sand of a Triassic stream. The broken parts, at the left, lie where they fell when the log was undermined by erosion. In the foreground are many small fragments, so-called "petrified chips." At the sky line above the baby's head may be seen the end of a log protruding from the rock. The brilliant colors of the rocks here suggest the name Painted Desert. Photograph by Willis T. Lee.

Plate XXIII. Zion Canyon, Utah.

Showing the southern end of The Narrows, where Virgin River has cut a narrow defile more than 3,000 feet deep through the Vermilion Cliff sandstone and overlying rocks. Photograph by Willis T. Lee.

with which we are familiar was slow. Those of the Jurassic period were probably similar to the modern egg-laying mammals of Australia.

The First Bird

The first bird that we know anything about lived in Jurassic time. The discovery of its remains was one of the spectacular finds in paleontology, for it appealed strongly to the popular imagination. This peculiar creature, *Archæopteryx*, had many distinctly reptilian characteristics and is regarded as a connecting link between reptiles and modern birds. The first indication of the existence of such a bird was found in 1860, when the impression of a single feather was found in the lithographic limestone of Solenhofen. A year later a nearly complete skeleton was discovered near Eichstadt.

Archæopteryx was about as large as a domestic pigeon. It had a small head, large eyes, nostrils situated well forward, and jaws set with many small teeth. It had no beak like that of modern birds. Its body was long and slender and lacked the large breast muscles of modern birds, which make them strong fliers.

Near the end of the Jurassic period a world-wide revolution occurred — some earth disturbance which caused the sea to retire from western America. With the succeeding period began a new order of events. The desert of early Jurassic time had been flooded by the sea in the later part of the period, and this sea in its turn retired, yielding the stage for other scenes.

On the floor abandoned by the Jurassic sea and on the surrounding lowlands great swamps were formed (Plate XXVII, A) and sluggish streams followed winding, shifting courses to the sea. Temporary lakes were formed in some places, and many bayous and lagoons. Through long ages the meandering streams swung from side to side, slowly filling the lakes with sand and the marshes with mud. This swampy area extended from Utah to Kansas and from New Mexico to Montana. It is now represented by rocks that the geologist calls the Morrison formation.

In the great swamps and along the winding streams of Morrison time there were developed a group of the most remarkable reptiles that the world has ever known. Many of them were swamp-loving creatures of enormous bulk. Some of them were vegetable eaters, which lived on soft vegetation and found safety in the streams and marshes. Others were ferocious killers that preyed on the more peaceful vegetable eaters.

Little is known of the kinds of vegetation that furnished food for these bulky creatures. Few fossil plants have been found in the Morrison formation. But the great size of these enormous reptiles implies an abundant supply of food.

Dinosaur National Monument

Some of the finest specimens of dinosaurs of Morrison time have been found in the plateau country of northeastern Utah. Because of its remarkable deposits of well preserved bones, a small tract of land that includes the best collecting ground has been set aside as the property of the public and called Dinosaur National Monument. This reserve was created in 1915 for the purpose of preserving the fossil bones. The monument embraces 80 acres of land, and its surface rocks are called by some the McElmo formation, although they are equivalent in age to the Morrison. The dinosaur skeletons are among the largest and the best preserved yet found.

Dinosaur bones were found many years ago at Como Bluff and elsewhere in Wyoming, and for a time the rocks in which they occur were called the Como beds. About the same time bones were found at Morrison and other places in Colorado, in rocks that were first called the Atlantosaurus beds but that were later called the Morrison formation. It is now known that the bone beds at all these localities are of the same geologic age, and the name Morrison is usually applied to all of them, but for those in Utah and other places in the Southwest the name McElmo is still used.

Although the Morrison is here described as a formation in the Jurassic system, some geologists believe that it should be included in the Cretaceous system rather than the Jurassic. It is the only representative of the long period between late Jurassic time and the middle part of the Cretaceous period.

Discovery of Dinosaurs in America

The great interest in the dinosaurs may justify an account of their discovery. But what constitutes discovery? If finding bones without recognizing them as such is discovery, the date and place of discovery remain unknown; if seeing large bones and leaving them undisturbed and undescribed constitutes discovery, Major Powell discovered them in 1869 at Flaming Gorge; if viewing certain dinosaur bones without recognizing them as dinosaurs is discovery, Professor Marsh discovered them in 1872 at Como, Wyo.; if unannounced collections constitute discovery, Mr. W. H. Reed must be given the credit. But if prompt public announcement is to be recognized, the credit seems to be equally divided between Mr. O. Lucas and Professor Edward D. Cope on the one hand and Professors Arthur Lakes and O. C. Marsh on the other.

The late Dr. S. W. Williston of Chicago University, who was closely associated with the several claimants and who has told the circumstances, holds that the discovery is to be attributed to "a state of mind." For years, according to him, beds containing great numbers of these bones had been studied by geologists of experience, but scarcely a scrap of bone had been recognized, although acres of surface were literally strewn with fragments. Some of these were so large as to tax the strength of a strong man to lift them. Pieces of dinosaur bone had been collected for years by tourists on the supposition that they were fossil wood. If this constitutes discovery there is no means of knowing when dinosaurs were discovered.

But in 1877 occurred what Professor Williston calls "a state of mind," by which three men, each unknown to the others, were impelled to find out what the fossils meant. W. H. Reed, in tramping over the hills of Wyoming in the winter and spring of 1877, found some fossil bones at Como Bluff and in the following autumn sent them to Professor O. C. Marsh at Yale University. Williston was sent by Marsh to Como Bluff, and in November, 1877, he and Reed opened the quarry from which much material was obtained later. Marsh had seen fragments of these bones at Como Bluff five years earlier but was then engrossed with other matters and paid little attention to them.

Mr. O. Lucas, an amateur botanist, found bones at Garden Park, near Canon City, Colo., in March, 1877. These he sent to Cope at Philadelphia, who described them. Later much material was collected at this locality by Marsh.

Professor Arthur Lakes found a large fossil vertebra near Morrison, Colo., in March, 1877. He sent this to Marsh, who described the fossil as belonging to *Titanosaurus* (*Atlantosaurus*) *immanis*. The beds were therefore long called the Atlantosaurus beds, but they were later named the Morrison formation.

The fossil bones are very abundant in some places, and many museums are well supplied with them. A small tail vertebra which I found in Wyoming years ago while collecting there with Professor Williston is doing service on my desk as a paper weight while I write this account. Carloads of the bones have been unearthed, and several nearly complete skeletons have

PLATE XXIV. THE GREAT WHITE THRONE, ZION NATIONAL PARK, UTAH.

View from west river trail through a narrow gorge in the nearby rocks The upper part consists of light colored, cross-bedded sandstone — the White Cliff sandstone; the part below is the Vermilion Cliff sandstone. Courtesy Union Pacific System.

been restored. The newest and perhaps the richest collecting ground is in Dinosaur National Monument.

In many ways the reptiles of Morrison time were the most singularly interesting creatures that ever lived. Some of them were the largest beings that ever walked on land. Reptiles reached their highest development at this time. They were the rulers on the land, in the water, and in the air. Their bones were preserved in great numbers in western North America, where conditions were especially favorable for their preservation, but some have been found in eastern North America, in Europe, in Africa, and in other parts of the world.

Como Bluff is classic ground to those who are interested in the fossil remains of these animals. In the bluff above the now abandoned station of Aurora W. H. Reed found the large petrified limb bone which Marsh recognized as belonging to some extinct animal then unknown. He enlisted the service of Mr. Reed, who, with others, carried on collecting here for ten years or more, and as a result of this and similar work done elsewhere Marsh was able to publish the restorations of dinosaurs that appeared from time to time in several publications.

The dinosaurs differed greatly in size, shape, structure, and habits. Some were plant eaters, others fed on flesh; some walked on four feet, others, with small, weak forelimbs, walked entirely upon strongly developed hind legs; some had reptile-like feet, others were bird footed; some had toes provided with long, sharp claws, others had flattened hoof-like nails. There were dinosaurs with small heads and dinosaurs with large heads. Some were bulky and cumbersome; others were small, light and graceful and in their structure resembled birds so closely that only the skilled anatomist can distinguish between their remains. Some enormous ones were clad in coats of bony armor, which gave them a bizarre appearance, like the old-time knight-errant or the modern war tank.

A Thunder Lizard

The largest herbivorous or plant-eating dinosaur whose fossil remains have been found in Como Bluff was the huge brontosaurus, or thunder lizard, as it was called by Professor Marsh. It was 70 feet long, stood 15 feet high at the hips, and had a long tail, an equally long neck, and a head that was only a little larger than that of a horse. The weight of such a creature has been variously estimated at 18 to 40 tons. This animal doubtless lived on luxuriant tropical vegetation, but how its enormous bulk could be sustained by such food as could pass through its ridiculously small mouth has caused much wonder. It is not certain whether the name thunder lizard was given to it because of its size, or because of the large sum — more than $10,000 — which Professor Marsh spent in excavating it and preparing it for exhibition.

Some dinosaurs that are even larger than the brontosaurus have been found more recently. A diplodocus now in the Carnegie Museum at Pittsburgh had a length of more than 84 feet. Some whose remains have still more recently been dug out in the Dinosaur National Monument are even larger.

At the time these creatures flourished western America was low, nearly level, and probably covered with tropical vegetation. It contained many wide, shallow streams and swampy areas, thus furnishing a congenial place for these sluggish, swamp-inhabiting creatures where they might wade leisurely about or float in the water; for it seems improbable that the enormous bulk of some of them could be sustained without lateral support such as they would obtain in water.

Prehistoric Combats

The life of the peaceful plant-eating dinosaur, however, was not always serene, for there lived at the same time dinosaurs whose powerful jaws, armed with long, sharp teeth, indicate that they lived on flesh. These animals are called allosaurs (Plate XXVII, B). That they fed upon large dinosaurs and smaller animals of their kind is indicated by the discovery of teeth of the carnivorous species together with the bones of their herbivorous contemporaries and of a skeleton of one of the herbivorous dinosaurs with bones scarred with the tooth marks and grooves corresponding exactly to the sharp pointed teeth of the allosaurs.

The allosaur was a powerful animal and is represented by skeletons over 20 feet long. The large bones of the limbs were hollow, as were many other parts of the skeleton, this structure facilitating rapid movement. The feet were armed with long, sharp claws, especially the forefeet, which were well adapted for catching and holding prey or for tearing and rending skin and flesh.

How old is it? This is one of the first questions asked when a fossil is exhibited. It is difficult to answer that question, and it is perhaps still more difficult for one who has given little thought to the subject to realize the great lengths of time represented by the geologic ages. The life of an individual is so short compared with the life of a race that great effort is required to realize even the march of human events. Yet the whole range of human history is only a very small fraction of a geologic period. W. D. Matthew, who has spent much time in working out the relative duration of the periods, has shown that if the age of reptiles should be represented by a single line extending across a page, the duration of human history would be represented by a line so short that it would be invisible to our eyes.

I have already referred to the first thunder lizard found by Professor Marsh and of the cost of obtaining the remains of that monster. A still better conception of the difficulties encountered and of the labor required for such work is given by Doctor Matthew in his description of a great skeleton, 66 feet long, of an animal whose weight in life is estimated at 38 tons. This skeleton, now in the American Museum of Natural History, was discovered north of Medicine Bow, Wyo., in 1898. The paleontologists spent the following summer in extracting it from the rock and in shipping it to the museum. Then for nearly two years workmen were busy chipping away the stone, and still more time was consumed in fixing the bones in place. At last, in 1905, after seven years' work, the great brontosaur was ready to receive visitors.

The proper posture of this great animal required much thought, for the dinosaur belongs to a lost race and has left no direct descendants. The fashions followed by this ancient monster and its habits have caused much discussion. It had a long, thick tail like a crocodile, a long, slim neck, a short, stout body, and massive legs like an elephant, only very much larger. The track of one foot covers nearly a square yard. Its bones were massive and heavy and were constructed with an elaborate pattern of braces and buttresses for the attachment of the huge muscles. The head was small, and the teeth indicate a vegetable diet.

After a general summary of the known characters of other lizards, it has been generally agreed that the thunder lizard lived chiefly in water; sometimes in muddy swamps, where he fed on succulent swamp vegetation; sometimes in rivers, where his massive, heavy bones made it possible for him to walk on the bottom under water where he was safe from his enemy, the allosaurus, while the plants on the bank were within easy reach of his long, flexible neck. However, Professor Williston thinks that Mrs. Brontosaurus must have walked out on land sometimes, "because reptile eggs can not hatch in water." Contemplate for a moment a nest of eggs laid by a 38 ton dinosaur!

The thunder lizard had several relatives, some larger and some smaller than himself. Among these may be mentioned diplodocus, a dinosaur that has become well known because of a splendid skeleton now in the Carnegie Museum at Pittsburgh. This skeleton has become famous through presentation of plaster casts of it to museums in foreign countries.

The first skeleton of diplodocus was found near Canon City, Colo., but better material was collected later at the Bone Cabin quarry near Medicine Bow, Wyo., a locality that has become classic to bone hunters because of the great number and variety of fossil bones found there. It was a kind of museum, perhaps better described as a graveyard, of all the reptiles of the period. From this quarry have been taken nearly 100,000 pounds of bones, representing seventy-three animals, and this weight does not include bones rejected as worthless, nor does it include the entire deposit. An unknown number of skeletons still remain in the rocks, and no doubt there are at least as many more as have been taken out.

Dinosaur Jewelry

Those whose interest in natural objects is confined to their commercial value may be interested in the utilization of dinosaur bones near Canon City, Colo., where large quantities of petrified bones have been cut into ornaments. The bones there were petrified by silicious material, producing red, brown and yellow jasper, with gray and white matrix, consisting in part of chalcedony. The replacement of different parts of the bone tissue by minerals of different colors has produced a variety of effects. The structure of the bone is shown well by spots and mottlings of dark jasper in a light-colored matrix. Some of the petrified bone polishes well and makes handsome ornamental stone. The fact that jewels are cut from petrified dinosaur bones is not extensively advertised, and many a man is wearing a watch charm, and many a woman carries a breastpin cut in the latest style from bones of a reptile that long ago went out of fashion.

Certain little gastropods lived at the time the dinosaurs flourished, and their shells, buried in the mud with the bones, have been petrified in carnelian-colored agate. One species of these gastropods was named in my honor. I am not certain just how much I should feel honored by having my name attached to a snail, but I feel some satisfaction in possessing a scarf pin consisting of a shell of *Valvata Leei* petrified in jewel agate.

Classic literature and the writings of later centuries abound in references to mythical beings that filled the imagination of the ancients. Classic art and the art of later centuries depicted these mythical beings in statuary, in painting, and in decorative architecture. The dinosaurs and other creatures of past ages make an appeal to popular imagination like that of some of the monsters of classic lore. Published pictures and descriptions of them are popular. The reproductions of the reptiles seem well adapted also for use in the field of caricature. When a cast of diplodocus was set up in South Kensington Museum, many amusing cartoons bearing upon the political events of the day appeared in the daily papers of England, in which this reptile was made to do service. It was made also to serve in commercial enterprise, as it was used by both the advertising agent and the modeler. "Diplodocus vases," bearing on their sides figures of the creature in high relief, were placed on the market in London by one of the best known firms engaged in the manufacture of majolica.

One of the largest known dinosaurs lived in Utah. Its bones were dug up in the Dinosaur National Monument and sent to Carnegie Museum, where it was named, in honor of Mrs. Andrew Carnegie, *Apatosaurus Louisæ*. In addition to being one of the largest creatures that ever walked on earth, its skeleton is said to be the most complete ever recovered of this remarkable race of extinct reptiles. So much of the skeleton was obtained (sixty-four out of the seventy-three vertebræ of the tail and other bones in like proportion) that there is little chance that the place or the natural relation of any of the bones is mistaken.

A Plated Lizard

The discovery of the extraordinary creature called stegosaurus was one of the great achievements of Professor Marsh, but since his day more nearly perfect skeletons have been found and placed on exhibition. The curious aspect of this animal makes it one of the most interesting of museum exhibits. This plated lizard was a vegetarian and was one of the strangest looking creatures of that strange time. The name plated lizard was given to it because of the bony plates on its back (Plate XXVIII, A). Some of these plates, although thin, were two or three feet across. They were held in upright position in parallel rows along the middle part of the back, extending from the base of the skull well down on the tail, the tip of which was armed with two pairs of long, bony spines. In some individuals these spines were over 3 feet in length. During life all the plates and spines were covered by a thick, horny skin.

The stegosaurs were about 20 feet long and stood about 10 feet high at the hips. The head was extremely small and lizard-like, the brain was small, the eyes were large, and the nostrils indicate a considerable power of smell. The great disproportion in length between the fore and hind legs, the small, pointed head, and the plates and spines made it so ugly that it may not have required other means of protection. Some passive protection, through repulsive ugliness or otherwise, seems to have been necessary, for its ludicrously diminutive brain suggests a mental power insufficient for conscious efforts at self-preservation.

Its want of brain capacity was compensated to some extent

by an enlargement of its spinal cord near the hips that was about ten times as large as its brain. This curious characteristic inspired Mr. B. L. Taylor of the Chicago Tribune to the following metrical effort:

Behold the mighty dinosaur,
Far-famed in prehistoric lore
Not only for his weight and strength
But for his intellectual length.
You will observe by these remains,
The creature had two sets of brains,

One in his head, the usual place,
The other at his spinal base;
Thus he could reason a priori
As well as a posteriori.
No problem bothered him a bit;
He made both head and tail of it.

So wise was he, so wise and solemn,
Each thought filled just a spinal column.
If one brain found the pressure strong,
He passed a few ideas along;
If something slipped his forward mind,
'Twas rescued by the one behind;

And if in error he was caught,
He had a saving afterthought;
As he thought twice before he spoke,
He had no judgment to revoke;
For he could think without congestion
Upon both sides of every question.

O gaze upon this model beast,
Defunct ten million years at least!

Plate XXV. The Three Patriarchs, Zion National Park, Utah.
The rock is red sandstone.

Where Triton and Titan Wrestled

A skeleton of a gigantic creature called allosaurus, 34 feet long and 8 feet high, now in the American Museum of Natural History at New York, was found at Como Bluff in 1879 and sent to Professor Cope. The bones remained boxed for years in Philadelphia until the collection was removed to the museum, where, in 1903, they were unpacked. It was then recognized that a treasure had come to light, for this is the finest specimen of its kind known.

Something of the appearance of this creature may be inferred from Plate XXVIII, A. The leathery skin; the long, powerful hind legs, with toes ending in claws; the small forelimbs, adapted to grasping its prey; the long heavy tail for balancing; and the powerful, heavily toothed jaws, all denote a predatory animal of great ferocity.

There were small flesh eaters as well as large ones. One of these, called *Ornitholestes*, was found at Bone Cabin quarry, Wyo. It had long hind legs for rapid movement, and short forelimbs with slender fingers adapted for grasping an active prey, such as the primitive birds, which were contemporaneous with it (Plate XXXVIII, B). The bird-catching dinosaur contrasted in many ways with its contemporaries. It was only about 7 feet long and was built on a plan designed for speed and agility. The bones were mere hollow shells, with walls as thin as paper. Its feet and hands were birdlike, the hands especially resembling those of the early birds in the great elongation of the first finger and the abbreviation of the other fingers.

The Sea and the Mountains

During all the time that the thick Jurassic deposits were accumulating in the West and during most of Lower Cretaceous time, the ancestral Rockies in Colorado and neighboring States were undergoing the last stages of destruction. Over the plains thus built up on the west and worn down on the east the sea water advanced in Upper Cretaceous time. At one time or another during this epoch the sea occupied the interior of North America from the Gulf of Mexico to the Arctic Ocean, and from Utah to the Mississippi River.

The country east of this interior sea was low and supplied little sediment, but the country west of it, the mountainous area that had furnished the great volumes of sand and silt during Jurassic and Lower Cretaceous time, seems to have been reëlevated and supplied the rock débris that gradually filled the interior basin. The advance of the sea over the plain must have been relatively rapid in a geologic sense, for the subsidence of a nearly level surface, even though very slow, would cause the strand line to move over it rather rapidly. During this advance of the sea, the sand and silt brought to it by streams were sorted by the waves, and the washed sand was deposited on the migrating beach. This sand hardened to form the group of beds which most geologists know as Dakota.

As the sea advanced the beach sand was covered with water, in which accumulated the material that formed the beds of shale, limestone, and sandstone of the Upper Cretaceous series of rocks. In the plateau country these rocks consist chiefly of sandstone. The material was derived from the highlands to the west, and in working eastward, whether carried by currents of the sea or washed over low-lying coastal plains by streams, the sand was deposited first and the fine silt was carried farther toward the east, where the rocks of this age consist of shale that originated as deposits of silt.

As the deposits accumulated the floor of the basin sank, but at no time was the water very deep. The sediments were distributed over the bed of the sea in thin, regular layers, which could have been formed only in shallow water or on low-lying coastal plains. Furthermore, the subsidence was not regular. For long periods the land remained stationary. During such periods the basin was filled near shore and the strand line was pushed far out into the basin.

The low-lying flats thus formed of sand and mud were favorable to the luxuriant growth of plants and to the formation of great swamps. In these swamps accumulated the vegetable matter which was later buried and turned into coal. In this way were formed great layers of sandstone, one of which caps Mesa Verde, in Mesa Verde National Park, and the extensive beds of coal found in the Cretaceous rocks of western America.

Chapter VII

CRETACEOUS SCENES

The third period of the Mesozoic era, or middle age, is called Cretaceous, and the rocks formed during this closing period of the era are known as the Cretaceous system. The chalk which gives its name to this system (the Latin word *Creta* means chalk, hence the name *Creta*ceous) was first studied in the Anglo-Parisian basin. The chalk cliffs of England have long been well known, and the chalky limestone of Kansas belongs in this system.

But although the name Cretaceous was originally given to rocks containing chalk, the rocks of the Cretaceous system as we now know it contain chalk in relatively few places. The name illustrates a common custom in geology and also one of the serious drawbacks resulting from this custom. Many rock formations are named for some local lithologic characteristic. The Exwyzee sandstone is a sandstone at Exwyzee, where it was first examined and named, but when this formation was traced laterally it was found that the Exwyzee sandstone consists of shale at some places and of limestone at other places. It therefore becomes necessary to explain that the Exwyzee formation is not everywhere a sandstone; it is a sandstone only at the place from which it was named.

During the Cretaceous period the sea overwhelmed the continents, submerging their low lands. The Cretaceous was a period of change in many ways — a period of advance toward present conditions. The lower orders of plants, which had held first place,

Plate XXVI. Rainbow Bridge, Utah.

A graceful natural arch of sandstone high enough to span the dome of the Capitol at Washington. It rises 309 feet above the stream that flows beneath it, and its abutments stand 278 feet apart. At its highest point the arch is 42 feet thick and 33 feet wide. Photograph by E. C. LaRue.

now took a subordinate position, and the higher orders of plants, such as we are familiar with today, assumed the leading rôle. The Cretaceous period marks the end of the age of reptiles. Some of these creatures, however, were then still numerous, but, like the plants, they were destined to give place to more modern forms. They did not long survive the geologic revolution that brought the Cretaceous period to an end. This revolution involved the emergence of continents from the sea, the formation of new ranges of mountains, and the introduction of animals of modern types.

Mesa Verde National Park

Rocks of Cretaceous age are conspicuously exposed in Mesa Verde National Park. The sandstone that caps Mesa Verde is harder than the shale that underlies it and has resisted erosion more strongly, so that it now forms the top of the most notable table-lands of southwestern Colorado. The Mesaverde formation, which was named from this mesa, is of commercial interest, for it contains vast deposits of coal, and it is of historic interest, for in the shelter of its protecting cliffs many of the ancient cliff-dwellers found safety.

The ruined houses of the cliff-dwellers (Plate XXIX), perched in almost inaccessible places, appeal powerfully to the imagination. Unfortunately those who dwelt in these natural fortresses left no written records. Their language is unknown. Many of the dwellings are well preserved and some of them contained utensils. But when we try to find who the cliff-dwellers were and why they sought such well-protected but difficult dwelling places we are baffled.

In 1888 Richard and Alfred Wetherill found the ruins known as Cliff Palace and Spruce Tree House. Since that time great numbers of other ruins have been found.

The interest in the ruins induced Congress to set aside Mesa

Verde as a national park in 1906, eighteen years after they were discovered and after many of them had been looted.

Mesa Verde National Park is an area of irregular outline containing 48,966 acres, situated on Mesa Verde, a Spanish term meaning Green Table. This mesa is one of the conspicuous geographic features of southwestern Colorado. It rises from the surrounding lowlands by steep, shaly slopes surmounted by a sandstone cliff. It reaches its maximum altitude, 8,575 feet, in Park Point, but its most conspicuous summit as seen from below is Point Lookout, which has a height of 8,429 feet. The walls of the mesa rise steeply about 2,000 feet above the floor of Mancos Valley on the east and about 2,300 feet above the floor of the broad Montezuma Valley, which lies north and west of the Park.

W. H. Holmes, who visited this mesa in 1875, says of it:

> The general level is well sustained by the massive layer of sandstone of the Upper Escarpment [now called Cliff House sandstone], not as an unbroken mass or block of strata, of course, for the erosive forces have invaded it on all sides and the edges are scalloped by a thousand gorges. Not only have the destroying forces encroached from the edges on all sides, but the mesa has been entirely severed by the canyon of the Rio Mancos, which cut through it from north to west. This cañon sends out a multitude of side cañons, which seem literally to have honeycombed the interior of the tableland. [The Rio Mancos swings to the west just south of the park boundary and into it empty all of the southward-flowing streams of the mesa.]

The outer rim of the mesa is intact. Viewed from the side the cap rock seems to be continuous, but in reality it is a mere skeleton. The outer rim has been likened to the tire of a wheel and the long strips of rock that separate the canyons to spokes of the wheel. The sandstone that caps the mesa was once continuous instead of trenched by long, narrow gorges, as it is now. Before it was trenched the surface sloped gently to the south, as the remnants of the cap rock do now.

The Little People

The modern Pueblo Indians of the Southwest, who dwell in community houses, are supposed to be the descendants of the cliff-dwellers. The objection of these Indians to the exploitation of the ruins by white men and their belief that the ancient dwellings are inhabited by spirits — the Little People — give color to this supposition. Their attitude was shown by their opposition to the installation of the telephone. As published by the National Park Service, the story runs as follows:

> Indians of today shun the ruins of the Mesa Verde. They believe them inhabited by spirits whom they call the Little People. It is vain to tell them that the Little People were their own ancestors; they refuse to believe it.
>
> When the National Park telephone line was building, in 1915, the Indians were greatly excited. Coming to the supervisor's office to trade, they shook their heads ominously.
>
> The poles wouldn't stand up, they declared. Why? Because the Little People wouldn't like such an uncanny thing as a telephone.
>
> But the poles were standing, the supervisor pointed out. All right, the Indians replied, but wait. The wires wouldn't talk. The Little People wouldn't like it.
>
> The poles were finally all in and the wires strung. What was more, the wires actually did talk and are still talking.
>
> Never mind, say the Indians, with unshaken faith. Never mind. Wait. That's all. It will come. The Little People may stand it for a while; but wait. The supervisor is still waiting.

Story of the Rocks

The mode of formation of the rocks, the differences in their hardness, why some contain fossil shells and others contain beds of coal and impressions of plants, are made clear by studies grouped under the head of geology. Why the mesa stands out so prominently above the surrounding country, why it is carved so ornately, how the sheltered nooks and alcoves were formed in which the cliff-dwellings were built, are made clear by a study of natural processes grouped under the head of physiography. The conclusion reached may be made sufficiently clear by presenting in story form the ancient events in order as they occurred, leading up to the production of the features as we see them.

The story may begin at the time when the oldest beds of the park were formed. These beds constitute the Mancos shale, so called from the town of Mancos, which stands on them. They are made up of mud that was deposited in Cretaceous time, when this part of North America was occupied by a sea. Mollusks lived and died in this sea and their shells were buried in the mud.

The sea was gradually filled with sediment, which finally consisted mainly of sand, until the water became shallow. At this time was formed the lower sandstone of the mesa rim, now exposed on Point Lookout, — the sandstone forming the lowest layer of the rocks called the Mesaverde formation.

A little later the sea was expelled entirely from this part of the basin, which became a low-lying coastal plain on which a great variety of plants grew, and swamps were formed in which accumulated the vegetable matter that later turned to coal, for the Mesaverde formation contains valuable beds of coal.

As time went on the swamps, with their beds of peat, were buried under sand and mud washed by the streams from the highlands farther west, and the alternating beds of coal, shale, and sand formed a mass about 400 feet thick. This mass, which lies upon the Point Lookout sandstone, has been named the Menefee formation, from Menefee Mountain, which stands east of the park, just south of the town of Mancos.

Conditions favorable to the accumulation of coal recurred many times in late Cretaceous time as new beds of sand accumulated on some new coastal plain. At some times the greater part of the basin was occupied by the sea; at other times sediments accumulated to such thickness that the water was expelled from

PLATE XXVII, A. SWAMP-DWELLERS OF MESOZOIC TIME.

A restoration by Charles R. Knight of "thunder lizards" (*Brontosaurus*), great amphibious dinosaurs whose remains are found in the Morrison formation. By permission of the American Museum of Natural History.

PLATE XXVII, B. MOUNTED SKELETON OF A HUGE CARNIVOROUS DINOSAUR (ALLOSAURUS), SHOWING THE SIZE OF THE REPTILE AS COMPARED WITH HUMAN BEINGS.

By permission of the American Museum of Natural History.

large parts of it. The resulting migration of the shore line has never been worked out in detail, but enough is known to indicate that the history of the time is complex.

Some of the coastal plains that were developed in later Cretaceous time were 200 or 300 miles wide and reached from central Utah eastward at least as far as the Rocky Mountains, in central Colorado.

The plants which furnished the material that formed coal left many records in the rocks. Innumerable leaf impressions and petrified trunks of trees have been found. Some of these impressions represent modern types of plants. In some places fossil leaves are particularly abundant. These plants belong to species that indicate a warm, moist climate for western America during Upper Cretaceous time.

Cretaceous Life

The animals of the Cretaceous epoch are no less interesting than those of the Jurassic. Reptiles were still rulers of earth, air, and sea. Their remains in America have been found chiefly in the West. The earlier horned dinosaurs differed in many ways from their descendants, especially in having a horn on the nose instead of horns over the eyes. The jaws of *Triceratops*, one of the later forms, terminated in a sharp beak, like that of a turtle, and the neck was protected by a scalloped bony shield called the frill.

The primitive horned dinosaurs ranged at least from New Mexico northward to Canada. They were peaceable plant-eaters and obviously needed protection from their enemies, the carnivorous dinosaurs. Hence the head was armed with horns, the neck was protected by the bony frill or shield, and the body was covered with a tough, scaly hide. These were the ancestors of *Triceratops*, which roamed the western plains at a later time (Plate XXXII, B).

The rulers of the air during this epoch were the flying reptiles called pterodactyls. Some of them were great dragons measuring 18 or 20 feet from tip to tip of wings. Their long jaws were armed with teeth, and their bat-like wings were formed of a thin membrane connecting greatly elongated fingers. These flying engines of destruction have been called the prototypes of the modern airplane.

Other inhabitants of the air in western America were certain toothed birds. These were connecting links between the reptile-like Jurassic birds, which had toothed jaws without beaks, and the modern birds, which have beaks but no teeth.

The fossil remains of the birds and of the reptiles of this time show many puzzling resemblances, which make it difficult to distinguish them. The question was debated whether *Archeopteryx* was a bird or a reptile, and it is now recognized that birds and reptiles are closely related. On this subject Dr. W. H. Ballou writes as follows in the Scientific American (1919):

> In the sense that clothes make the man, feathers make the bird. Hence the bird is merely a flying reptile, feathered more or less, according to species. Man has little of the reptile structure, but a bird has little else. Feathers, then, merely conceal the reptile. When Robin Redbreast lifts up his head and pours out his morning song, the brain that guides it is almost identical with that of the young alligator, which, while it can not sing, bays and roars pretty loudly. Mrs. Robin lays an egg and so does Mrs. Alligator.

The rulers of the Mesozoic sea were the swimming reptiles, the mosasaurs. These were powerful swimmers and found their way to all parts of the interior Cretaceous sea. Their long, slim bodies have suggested the name ancient sea serpents. Their powerful jaws were armed with long, conical, sharp-pointed teeth. These they used for capturing prey and in fighting among themselves.

Fossil bones of mosasaurs marked by the teeth of other

mosasaurs have been found. One of these bitten bones has a tooth embedded in it. The victor in the combat did not escape without injury. Apparently the victim struggled so fiercely as to break away from its enemy. The wound healed, incasing the enemy's tooth, and later, after the death of the escaped mosasaur, the bone, with the tooth in it, was buried and preserved as a fossil.

Chapter VIII

TERTIARY LANDSCAPES

The Cenozoic, the last of the geologic eras, includes two periods of geologic time — the Tertiary period (the age of mammals) and the Quaternary period (the age of man).

Many years ago the groups of sedimentary rocks were named in order from oldest to youngest — Primary, Secondary, Tertiary, and Quaternary. The last two names have survived, but the first two are no longer used as names of geologic periods.

The rocks of Tertiary age in America are chiefly of upland or non-marine origin and contain relatively few fossils, but Tertiary sediments that accumulated in sea water near the ancient margin of the continent contain great numbers of fossils. In fact, at some places the Tertiary rocks consist almost wholly of shells. A slab of rock containing such shells led to an incident which, although it occurred several years ago, still remains fixed in my memory.

Language of the Rocks

I was looking at material in the fossil room of the National Museum when a man and a boy entered and leisurely began to examine the curiosities.

They stopped before a slab of rock like that pictured in Plate XLVI, which contained many fossil shells, some of them standing out plainly, others deeply imbedded in the rock.

"Dad! What are these things?" inquired the boy, pointing to the fossils.

"Words," replied the man, "Those are all words."

I looked up in surprise, prepared to correct the statement. But I did not correct it. Something in the expression of the man kept me from interfering.

The boy seemed to be less surprised than I was. To him the museum was a house of wonders. Everything was strange. Nothing was beyond belief. He had not yet developed the "critical mind of wisdom." Instead of showing surprise he innocently asked, "Is this another Egyptian tablet like the one we saw in the other room?"

"Something like that," replied the man, "except that this language is much older than the Egyptian." "Do you remember," he asked, drawing a piece of paper from his pocket on which were some curious characters, "what these words are?"

"Yes," replied the boy, interested at once. And then the lesson in Egyptology was rehearsed.

"Very good! Now, the words of this other language are not more difficult than the Egyptian." "This word," continued the man, pointing to a coiled shell, "is *gastropod.* The one near it is *pelecypod.* For the present you may say *snail* and *clam.* Some day you may learn that these words tell a story about animals that lived long ago."

"That must be a strange language," ventured the boy, with a questioning glance to see if his father was really in earnest.

"Yes, to many it is a strange language, but to those who know it, its meaning is very clear.

"It is the language of creation. This slab of rock is a page from the story of the ancient inhabitants of the earth. The fossil-words may seem strange to you now, but later you will learn that the language may be translated and that it tells many a fascinating story."

The boy seemed skeptical, and the father, accepting his challenge to read this particular story, said:

"Notice first that this is a thin layer of rock, split away from other layers that once lay above and below it. They were piled up, one above another, like the leaves in a story book. This leaf tells among other things that the part of the story of the earth which it contains is near the end, just as page 200 in a book tells you that its part of the story is near the end.

"This slab of fossils comes from high up in the pile of leaves. The fossil words tell that it is from the part of the story which is called *Tertiary* and from the chapter known as *Miocene.* The fossils say that about the middle of the time known to geologists as the Tertiary period shallow sea water covered the part of Virginia where this rock was found. In the water of this sea lived many snails and clams. Their shells were buried in the mud, and in time this mud hardened to rock.

"Long afterward the sea bottom was raised out of the water and became land. The rain and the streams wore away the softer parts of the rock, leaving the harder parts standing as hills and bluffs."

"Dad," inquired the lad, who was naturally more interested in the fossils than he was in the story, which he could only half understand, "are many of the rocks covered with fossils like this one?"

"No! Few of them are so plainly marked. But there are many places in river bluffs where specimens just as good might be found."

"Say, Dad!" exclaimed the boy with enthusiasm, "Let's go after some of our own. I want to spring this on Bob and Skinny. I'll bet they never heard a story like this."

Then I received another mild shock, for, instead of rebuking the boy for harboring an unworthy motive, his father promised to show him where he could find the shells and to help him in framing a story for his boy friends.

Here was the university professor of the future receiving his early training. For what is a teacher except one who delights in telling the "Bobs" and the "Skinnies" and all other comers about things that interest him?

Bryce Canyon

The Tertiary rocks, like those of each of the older systems, are represented in a national park, or what will some day be a national park. Bryce Canyon (Plate XXX) was made a national monument by presidential proclamation in 1923, and during the following year Congress provided that it shall become a national park when all the land within its borders shall be the property of the Government.

Bryce Canyon is a bowl-shaped cavity that is eroded to a depth of nearly 1,000 feet into one of the high plateaus of Utah. The bowl is about three miles long and two miles wide and is open at one end. The brilliantly colored Tertiary rocks in which it is formed are eroded into a wilderness of pinnacles and spires and monuments, all carved in a profusion of ornamental designs. Some are graceful, others are grotesque; some are beautiful and impressive, others are bizarre. But all are intensely fascinating.

Bryce Canyon contains an astonishing array of startling beauty and grotesque grandeur. Those who enjoy flights of fancy can see here castles and cathedrals, Greek temples and Chinese pagodas, mosques and minarets and monuments in endless, bewildering variety. Those who would look beneath the superficial form may discover here an impressive exhibition of one of the processes by which highlands are torn down and carried to the sea. The sedimentary rocks that were built up layer on layer throughout the long ages of early Tertiary time are now being reduced to fragments and washed into Colorado River for transportation to the sea.

In geologic history, as in human history, a system built up laboriously in one age is torn down in a succeeding age and replaced by another system.

In general it may be said that the Tertiary period was ushered in by a world-wide revolution. Seas changed places and mountains arose where sea water had been. Whole races of animals were obliterated and new races took their places. Whole floras or groups of plants disappeared and new floras appeared.

It was this revolution that eventually ended the dominance of reptiles and introduced mammals as the rulers of the earth. The reptiles did not at once disappear, nor did the mammals at once spring into prominence. Indeed, the reptiles have not yet disappeared, nor have the mammals yet developed beyond the possibility of improvement. Nevertheless the Tertiary is known as the age of mammals.

At the beginning of the Tertiary period great geographic changes occurred in western America. The sea that had covered the central part of the continent was expelled at the end of Cretaceous time. Mountains arose in its place and plateaus were lifted out of the sea. However, some parts of the West remained low, and on them gathered the sand and clay derived from the newly formed highlands.

The marine life of the region was destroyed. The great "sea serpents" — the mosasaurs — disappeared, as did also the peculiar toothed birds and flying dragons. But some of the forms of land life persisted with relatively little change. Some dinosaurs remained, but not the particular species that had lived in Cretaceous time. The plants, too, underwent a change. The unrecorded interval of time between the two periods, although short in a geologic sense, was long enough to permit the removal by erosion of many thousands of feet of rock from the newly made mountains.

An Age of Violence

The geologist thinks of the Tertiary period as one of tumultuous earth action. Earthquakes were then doubtless violent, and

Plate XXVIII, A. " Behold the Mighty Dinosaur, Famous in Prehistoric Lore."

A restoration by C. W. Gilmore of the U. S. National Museum of an armored reptile (*Stegosaurus*) of Mesozoic time, whose remains are found in the Morrison formation.

Plate XXVIII, B. Restoration of a Bird-catching Dinosaur (Ornitholestes) Represented in the Act of Capturing One of the Primitive Birds Called Archaeopteryx.

By permission of the American Museum of Natural History.

PLATE XXIX. SPRUCE-TREE HOUSE, AN ANCIENT CLIFF DWELLING IN MESA VERDE NATIONAL PARK, COLORADO.

Mesa Verde hides in its barren canyons the well-preserved ruins of a civilization that passed out of existence long ago. Photograph by Herbert W. Gleason. By courtesy of National Park Service.

volcanic eruptions were numerous. Apparently the slow-moving dinosaurs found life too strenuous for endurance, for they disappeared forever soon after the beginning of the Tertiary period. Several explanations have been offered for their extinction. Some have held that the bulky creatures were not able to endure the earthquake shocks. Others have maintained that their disappearance was due to the prevalence of volcanic dust, which choked them. Still others believe that their eggs were eaten by the increasing swarms of diminutive mammals. The explanations thus offered are all somewhat fanciful, and there seems to be no more reason for seeking a special explanation of the disappearance of the dinosaurs than of that of the mammoth or of any other of the thousands of species of animals that flourished for a time and then became extinct.

In the plateau country the earth's activities were somewhat different from those in the Rocky Mountains. There were great crustal movements and a general rise of land. But this rise produced table-lands rather than mountain ranges.

However, several small groups of mountains were formed, in which molten rock seeking a way of escape from the interior failed to reach the surface, but became lodged between subsurface beds. These intrusions raised the rocks above them until they looked like huge blisters. Instead of pouring from some opening in the crust of the earth and spreading over the surface, the molten matter lifted the layers of rock near the surface into great domes, beneath which it gathered, cooled, and solidified. These once molten cores of the mountains are known to geologists as laccoliths. Erosion has removed the domed strata and exposed some of these laccoliths, but the upbowed sedimentary rocks in others, as in Navajo Mountain, in southern Utah, still conceal the igneous rocks which domed them.

Near the western edge of the plateau country sedimentary rocks ranging in geologic age from Cambrian to early Tertiary are found in full thickness. Originally these rocks extended beyond their present limit, but how much beyond no one can tell. They were eroded away after the upheaval in the early part of the Tertiary period. Over large areas sedimentary rocks thousands of feet thick were stripped from the underlying crystalline rocks. On the newly formed floor of ancient rocks were piled mountainous masses of lava. These early lavas formed light-colored varieties of igneous rock called andesite and rhyolite (Plate XXXI).

At some time during the Tertiary period the earth's crust in the plateau country was broken into huge blocks, and these blocks were lifted, tilted, and generally disturbed. Doubtless these disturbances extended over thousands of centuries. Doubtless also they were accompanied by violent earthquakes and volcanic eruptions, for in the canyon country there are volcanic rocks of many different epochs.

This elevation of the plateaus and the erosion following it produced much of the natural scenery for which western America is famous.

Tertiary Animals

The Tertiary period was a time of rapid change in the form and habits of living creatures as well as change in the physical aspects of the country. The reptiles that were dominant in the preceding age became subordinate in Tertiary time. Soon after the beginning of this period the great dinosaurs disappeared and mammals took their place as rulers of the earth.

Among the reptiles of early Tertiary time were three peculiar forms — the great carnivorous dinosaur, *Tyrannosaurus* — a name expressive of his ferocious appearance; *Triceratops*, the three-horned dinosaur; and *Anchylosaurus*, an armored creature that has been called an animated fortress.

In the first of these monsters, known as *Tyrannosaurus rex*

(Plate XXXII, A), the king of tyrant lizards, the flesh eaters reached their apex, for *rex* was 47 feet long and stood nearly 20 feet high. His head was 4 feet 3 inches long and his powerful jaws were armed with teeth 3 to 6 inches long and an inch thick. The sharp claws that terminated his enormous toes were 6 to 8 inches long and were curved like the talons of an eagle. The fore-arms were so small as to indicate that *rex* must have walked entirely on his powerful hind legs. A nearly perfect skull of this creature is exhibited in the American Museum of Natural History, in New York City. It is with a feeling of awe that the observer stands before this huge head and contemplates a beast of such terrible ferocity.

Rex had several contemporaries that were scarcely less formidable than himself. One called *Albertosaurus*, which lived in Canada, is said to have rivaled *rex* in both size and ferocious appearance. Against the weapons of such adversaries as *Tyrannosaurus* and *Albertosaurus* the enormous horns of *Triceratops* and the heavy protective armor of *Anchylosaurus* seem to have been necessary for mere existence.

An Animated Fortress

Anchylosaurus was a beaked dinosaur related to the older armored dinosaur *Stegosaurus*, which had flourished in the same region several millions of years earlier. Like his ancient ancestor, *Anchylosaurus* was a vegetable eater of peaceful nature, without fighting tusks or aggressive armament of any kind. He was a contemporary of the tyrant lizards and therefore needed protective covering. His entire back was covered with flat bony plates. He was low in stature, had a short, blunt head, and carried on the end of his thick, heavy tail a large triangular bony club. His eye was protected by a cup-like bony shutter, like the visor of a helmet, which he could close over the eyeball.

All the vulnerable parts of this animated fortress were protected by bony armor. The legs were short, massive, and straight, ending probably in elephant-like feet. The "horned toad," one of the small modern lizards of the western plains, is not very different in external appearance from the armored dinosaur except in size.

Another modern armored lizard, the moloch, found in Australia, resembles *Anchylosaurus* in repulsive ugliness and in the possession of elaborate protective armor.

Like the modern banded armadillo, *Anchylosaurus* maintained a secure existence behind his protective covering. He has been called the most ponderous animated citadel the world has ever seen, and he evidently presented a defensive exterior that was proof against the attacks of his contemporary, the tyrant king, who did not exterminate the race. Some of the bones of these animals of demoniacal appearance have been found in the Hell Creek beds of Montana; others have been found in rocks of about the same age in Alberta. They evidently roamed over a large part of the western interior of North America.

Fall of Reptilian Imperialism

Here we may profitably note that the most perfectly armed and most powerfully equipped natural fighters that the world has ever known lived side by side with the most perfectly armored and the most completely protected creatures that imagination can picture. Perhaps those who are today advocating the disarmament of nations have read the lesson that geology teaches so plainly and are trying to apply nature's remedy, for *Tyrannosaurus*, the militant king, and *Anchylosaurus*, the animated fortress, were "scrapped" and fossilized together.

It may further be pointed out that these most powerful fighters and most perfectly armored beings were the last of their race. Reptilian nature had done its best — or worst — in both offensive and defensive armament, and as if recognizing the futility of

PLATE XXX. PINNACLES AND SPIRES IN BRYCE CANYON, UTAH.

The rocks are highly colored and are carved by erosion into monuments that show astonishing variety of form. Courtesy Union Pacific System.

Plate XXXI. Canyon of Yellowstone River as Seen from an Airplane; Looking Upstream.

The canyon is eroded to a depth of more than 1,000 feet in volcanic rock of Tertiary age. Official photograph U. S. Army Air Service.

further endeavor these reptiles perished from the face of the earth.

Bones of the dinosaur *Triceratops* (three-horned-face), so named in allusion to the three horns on the head (Plate XXXII, B), are found also in rocks of early Tertiary age. Over each eye was a long, massive horn, directed forward and terminating in a sharp point, and the nose usually bore a third but smaller horn. A mounted skeleton of a *Triceratops* in the National Museum at Washington, D. C., is about 20 feet long and stands 8 feet high at the hips. Some skulls measure more than 8 feet, over a third the length of the animal. This great length of head is due largely to the remarkable bony frill, which projects backward over the neck like a fireman's helmet.

That *Triceratops*, although a plant eater, was a fighter and often engaged in combat appears to be shown by its broken and healed bones. A dinosaur horn in the National Museum bears witness to such an encounter. It was broken during the life of the animal and healed to a rounded stump. Although *Triceratops* had an enormous head it had a smaller brain in proportion to its size than the least intelligent land animal of the present time. Fossil impressions of the skin show that it was covered with hexagonal scales.

As the dinosaurs retired from the stage of action creatures of higher intelligence and more supple movement, capable of adapting themselves to the rapidly changing physical conditions of Tertiary time, took their places.

Physical Records

The fossil remains of great numbers of these early mammals have been collected in museums and their significance has been pointed out. But although fossils are excellent records of geologic events they are not the only records. The attitude of the sedimentary rocks — whether upturned or flat–lying — the canyons, the peaks, and the plains all tell their story.

Two general types of sedimentary beds of Tertiary age occur in North America — those near the borders of the continent, formed wholly or partly in the sea, and those in the interior of the continent, consisting of rock débris deposited chiefly by streams. The Rocky Mountains of Colorado and other ranges farther west, which began to rise at the beginning of the Tertiary period and continued to rise intermittently during that period, furnished this material. The streams that drained these newly made mountains carried the material to the lower lands and spread it out in broad sheets.

On the plains, near the meandering streams, lived a great variety of mammals. The ever-changing physical conditions of the region, brought about by the repeated rise of the mountains, the volcanic disturbances, and the shifting of the streams, forced changes in the habits of these animals. Those that could adapt themselves to the new conditions survived; those that could not do so perished.

The Tertiary was a period of physical change and of rapid evolution of life. It was the schooling time during which animal life reached the high degree of perfection that culminated in man. It is evident that the improvement in the race of animals was effected through struggle with a constantly varying succession of difficulties. The relative tranquillity that prevailed during most of the Cretaceous period was followed by great changes.

Activity was the order in Tertiary time. Nature was busy reconstructing continents, building mountains, and generally changing the complexion of the face of the earth. The inhabitants of the earth had to adapt themselves to the changing conditions or perish. The old order was replaced by the new. The revolution that introduced the Tertiary period was the "world war" of geology. The following period, during which all things became new, was a time of reconstruction, of advancement and rapid evolution, a time when the life of the world was greatly improved.

The Tertiary period has been subdivided into four epochs. These epochs, named in order from oldest to youngest, are the Eocene, Oligocene, Miocene, and Pliocene. The Eocene epoch was very long, and by many geologists it is subdivided into Eocene proper and an older epoch called Paleocene. The Paleocene saw the extinction of the dinosaurs and the rise of the primitive mammals. The Eocene proper saw the great development of the larger mammals.

Some of the Eocene mammals had a generalized structure — that is, they possessed capability of development along different lines. One of the early mammals, for example, was an ancestor of flesh-eating creatures through one line of descent and of herb-eaters through another line. Many of these first mammals were curious looking creatures, such as *Eobasileus*, the *Loxolophodon* referred to in the verses quoted beyond. This great giant had a curiously shaped, long head with two pairs of bony protuberances resembling horns, one pair at the posterior end of the skull and one midway. A smaller single protuberance adorned the nose, and a pair of great tusks extended downward from the upper jaw.

Ancient Mammals

The skull of *Eobasileus* and the skulls of some of his associates seem to indicate clearly why many of the prehistoric monsters did not survive. These extinct giants, although as large as elephants, had brains that were ridiculously small. Their intelligence seems to have been inferior even to that of the modern rhinoceros. Judging from their small brain capacity it would seem that these early Tertiary monsters scarcely knew enough to take care of themselves. They perished. There were no asylums in Tertiary time for the weak minded.

One of the enemies of *Eobasileus* was the creodont, a wolf-like creature, one of the first flesh-eating mammals.

But other kinds of Tertiary mammals were able to meet the requirements of their age. Very early in the age of mammals there lived a group of creatures called the Condylarthra. These were probably the ancestors of such modern hoofed animals as the horse, the tapir, and the rhinoceros. They had five toes on each foot and each toe was tipped with a small hoof, such as is seen on each toe of some modern animals; others had claws.

These beings gave rise to several races, and each race followed its own particular line of development. One race retained all five hoofed toes on each foot; another lost all but two and developed into the split-hoofed animals, such as sheep and cattle; still another race lost all but one toe, thus producing the horse and other single-hoofed animals.

The First Horse

The earliest known direct ancestor of the horse yet found is *Eohippus*, a little creature about the size of a fox, which had four functional toes on each forefoot and three on each hind foot. Other toes were only vestiges or were wholly missing. But *Eohippus* had possibilities of development. Through growth and change and evolutionary development there appeared *Orohippus*, then *Miohippus* and *Pliohippus*, and finally *Equus*, the modern horse.

The Tertiary period was one during which broad, grassy upland plains were formed in western America. Doubtless then, as now, animals that lived in the open, without the protection of forests in which to conceal themselves, must have been able either to defend themselves when attacked or to flee from their enemies. The ancestral horse was not a fighter, but it had the capacity of developing speed, and the history of the horse through the geologic epochs, as well as through the period of human history,

Plate XXXII. A. A Tyrant King (Tyrannosaurus Rex).

Restoration by Charles R. Knight of a huge carnivorous dinosaur of early Tertiary or Paleocene time. It was a formidable creature about 40 feet in length, with jaws 5 feet long, armed with long, sharp teeth adapted to tearing flesh. To the right is a group of reptiles (Triceratops) which were contemporaries of the tyrant king. By permission of the American Museum of Natural History.

Plate XXXII, B. Old Three-horn-face (Triceratops).

A restoration of the last of the dinosaurs by C. W. Gilmore of the U. S. Natural Museum. The illustration shows the small horn on the nose, a large horn over each eye, the bony frill on the neck, and the armored hide.

shows improvement in the mechanism that makes for swift movement and great endurance.

Apparently, as time went on, ancestral horses found increasing need for speed, and in striving for greater agility they rose more and more on to the ends of the toes, as the modern dancer rises for the same purpose. As evolution progressed the horse depended more and more on the middle toe, which was gradually developed at the expense of the side toes, and these in time became mere vestiges and at last disappeared, leaving only the middle toe.

Poetical Paleontology

The development of *Eohippus* into the modern horse was made the subject of the following verses by Charlotte Perkins Stetson.[1]

There was once a little animal
  No bigger than a fox,
And on five toes he scampered
  Over Tertiary rocks.
They called him Eohippus,
  And they called him very small,
And they thought him of no value —
  When they thought of him at all;
For the lumpish Dinoceras
  And Coryphodon so slow
Were the heavy aristocracy
  In days of long ago.

Said the little Eohippus,
  "I am going to be a horse!
And on my middle finger-nails
  To run my earthly course!
I'm going to have a flowing tail!
  I'm going to have a mane!
I'm going to stand fourteen hands high
  On the psychozoic plain!"

[1] In This Our World, p. 95. Small, Maynard & Co., 1898.

The Coryphodon was horrified,
  The Dinoceras shocked;
And they chased young Eohippus
  But he skipped away and mocked.
Then they laughed enormous laughter,
  And they groaned enormous groans,
And they bade young Eohippus
  Go view his father's bones.
They said "You always were as small
  And mean as now we see,
And that's conclusive evidence
  That you're always going to be.
What? Be a great, tall, handsome beast,
  With hoofs to gallop on?
Why! You'd have to change your nature!"
  Said the Loxolophodon.

They considered him disposed of,
  And retired with gait serene;
That was the way they argued
  In "the early Eocene."

These verses differ rather sharply from some attempts to incorporate scientific material in popular writing, for in them no distortion of fact lurks under poetic license. *Dinoceras* and *Coryphodon* (Plate XXXIV, A) were contemporaries of the ancestral horse, and the middle finger nail on these animals corresponds to the hoof of the horse. It may be noted that the argument of the small-brained *Loxolophodon* relative to possibilities of self-improvement has a strangely familiar sound.

Although rocks of later Tertiary age are not found in the canyon country, those rocks contain records that lead up to events that are an essential part of the story of the canyon country. At some places near the borders of the North American continent Tertiary sediments were being laid down in water to form records such as those illustrated in Plate XLVI, which shows a variety of fossil shells preserved in great perfection.

In the western interior of the continent sediments from the recently formed highlands were spread out over the broad upland plains and entombed the bones of innumerable animals, such as *Titanotherium* and *Protoceros*, the American rhinoceros, the four-horned deer, and several kinds of camels.

These were some of the ancient inhabitants of North America in Tertiary time before the high plateaus and their canyons came into being.

Chapter IX

QUATERNARY LANDSCAPES

The Quaternary period is the last of the geologic ages, the one in which we live. It includes the Pleistocene epoch, known generally as the Great Ice Age, in which primitive man appeared, and the Recent epoch, in which the human race attained supremacy over all other living beings.

Let us remember that Grand Canyon is cut in old beds of rock, Zion Canyon in beds of middle age, and Bryce Canyon in younger beds. But although the beds were laid down in times far apart, the forms and features of the land in all three canyons were produced by recent erosion.

Most of the land forms in all our national parks and elsewhere, which constitute the impressive scenery of the West, were produced by Pleistocene erosion or in part by Recent erosion, though several of the show places of America are notably Pleistocene. Perhaps first among these should be mentioned Glacier National Park (Plate XXXV), for its glaciers may be regarded as survivors from the Great Ice Age.

Yosemite Valley also is distinctively Quaternary, for its wonderful scenery was shaped by the glacial ice which once filled it. Conspicuous highlands like those of the Rocky Mountain National Park, whose charm depends on mountain peak and gorge, are doubtless due chiefly to Pleistocene action, although their shaping may have begun in an earlier epoch.

Glacier National Park

Glacier National Park, in northern Montana, although famous for its rugged mountains and gem-like lakes, is probably best known for its glaciers, some sixty in number, and for its steep-walled gorges, which were shaped by the powerful precursors of these relatively small bodies of ice, chiefly at a time when ice filled the valleys and covered much of the mountainous area.

Yosemite National Park

The ability of a stream of ice to shape a rock gorge is shown clearly in Yosemite Valley (Plate XXXVI). Those who have been entranced with its beauty and grandeur will doubtless agree with John Muir, who describes it as including—

> innumerable lakes and waterfalls and smooth, silky lawns, the noblest forests, the loftiest granite domes, the deepest ice-sculptured canyons, the brightest crystalline pavements, and snowy mountains soaring into the sky twelve and thirteen thousand feet, arrayed in open ranks and spiry-pinnacled groups, partially separated by tremendous canyons and amphitheaters; gardens on their sunny brows, avalanches thundering down their long white slopes, cataracts roaring, gray and foaming in the crooked rugged gorges, and glaciers in their shadowy recesses, working in silence, slowly completing their sculptures; newborn lakes at their feet, blue and green, free from or encumbered with drifting icebergs like miniature Arctic Oceans, shining, sparkling, calm as stars.

This wondrous valley is the work of water and ice. It was once a tortuous river valley, in which the Merced River cut deep into the rocks. Then the valley was filled with ice, which broadened it, cut away its irregularities, and finally left it in the form which now delights the eye of every observer.

Rocky Mountain National Park

Striking natural scenes, great as well as small, may be the results of relatively recent erosion. The great ridges, peaks, and canyons of our western mountains, as well as the smaller features of the landscape, were shaped chiefly in the Quaternary period.

Impressive mountains and valleys are found in many of our national parks, but one park especially has been created as representative of the finest scenery in the Rocky Mountain region. On June 26, 1915, a part of the Front Range in Colorado, including Long's Peak (Plate XIII), which rises to an altitude of 14,255 feet, was set aside as the Rocky Mountain National Park. The appeal of this park is varied. Here the visitor may find many modern conveniences, or he may bivouac by rock and stream in the primitive forest.

Like Bunyan's pilgrims, who in the course of their progress came to the "delectable mountains," the modern pilgrims come — 234,000 of them, in 1925 — to find their hearts' desire in the delectable mountains of the Snowy Range. Here they realize the dreams that illuminated the weeks and months of vacation planning.

The Snowy Range is a part of the Continental Divide. Here craggy peaks and rock-ribbed gorges form many an inspiring scene. The mountain monarchs stand in calm dignity and stalwart nobility, cloud-encircled and snow-crowned.

This noble range is a succession of lofty summits that rise above the altitude at which trees can live. Several glaciers, preserved in sheltered gorges, remind us of the time, thousands of years ago, when ice filled all the gorges in the higher parts of the range.

The Rocky Mountain National Park is noted chiefly for the variety of its mountain landscape. The land forms are results of the action of stream and frost and ice as they carved the granite mass into peak and gorge.

A time there was when the waves of an open sea rolled unhindered by rock or shoal where Long's Peak now stands. When the mountains arose out of the sea, the covering of sedimentary rocks was eroded away and the underlying crystalline rocks were attacked and carved into the delectable mountains.

Caverns

Caverns have been mentioned as the fourth type of natural objects that may be regarded as distinctively Quaternary. America is rich in caverns. Many of them have been explored; others have never been entered.

Three types of caverns may be noted: those consisting of great, complicated solution cavities in limestone, slightly adorned, like Mammoth Cave in Kentucky; those represented by Carlsbad Cavern in New Mexico (Plate XXXIX), in which the solution cavities are so generally filled with onyx marble that they are attractive chiefly because of their adornments; and those formed in igneous rock during the closing stages of volcanic eruption, when molten rock flowed from beneath a solidified crust, leaving long, irregularly shaped subterranean galleries. As scoriaceous lava is a poor conductor of heat, ice accumulates in these caverns, so that many of them are known as ice caves. An example is one in New Mexico known as the Cerro de la Bandera ice cave.

Mammoth Cave

Probably every reader of this account knows something of Mammoth Cave. Many people have visited it and many others recall the wonder aroused by the meager accounts of this cave in school geographies.

Mammoth Cave, a cavern in limestone in south-central Kentucky, is the best known of the many caves in this land of Daniel Boone. In fact, the limestone over an area of some 8,000 square miles is so honeycombed by solution that surface streams are rare. The surface waters find their way through sink holes into underground streams, which thread their way through ramifying subterranean passages. It has been estimated that Kentucky has 100,000 miles of open caverns.

Mammoth Cave is entered through an inconspicuous opening

on a forest-covered hillside overlooking Green River. Inside the opening the visitor pauses for a few minutes to light the lamps and get his "cave eyes." The first scenes of interest cluster about the old saltpeter vats, where nitrate was obtained for the gunpowder that saved America in the War of 1812. Many of the vats, which are built of split logs, have stood unchanged for more than 100 years and are still filled with the "peter dirt" from which the nitrate was leached.

At the inner end of the line of vats is a large open space known as Booth's Theatre (Plate XLI). This great unadorned space may be regarded as typical of Mammoth Cave. It is "grand, gloomy, and peculiar." The cave is mammoth but not beautiful. Its avenues are endless but unadorned. Mile after mile and hour after hour we walk between barren walls of limestone.

In the lowest chambers of the cave, 360 feet underground, is Echo River and its neighbor, the River Styx. Although there is nothing beautiful about them, these streams seem to have a peculiar fascination for visitors. The fascination seems to be due to the repulsive ugliness of the weird scenes. During times of flood the muddy back water from Green River enters the cave and deposits mud, which remains slimy for a long time after the flood waters have subsided.

The weird fascination of the place is enhanced by the blind fishes in the water and the presence on the walls of eyeless insects making their way over the rocks by means of long sensitive feelers. The timid, here, are wont to cower in fear, and the bolder spirits to recall Coleridge's lines

"Where Alph, the sacred river ran
Through caverns measureless to man
Down to a sunless sea."

Probably the most interesting parts of Mammoth Cave are those that exhibit the so-called domes. The surface waters that

PLATE XXXIII. A VOLCANIC CONE ON MOUNT SHASTA, CALIFORNIA.

On this isolated peak (14,161 feet high) the storm clouds deposit snow which forms mountain glaciers. In the midst of the ice fields stands a volcanic cone of recent origin, built up about some vent from which lava was ejected. Here glacial frost and volcanic heat carry on an endless struggle for supremacy. Official photograph U. S. Army Air Service.

make their way downward into the soluble limestone dissolve passageways, which in some places are of magnificent proportions, as at Hovey's Cathedral (Plate XLII), in the new entrance to Mammoth Cave. These domes reach their climax in Mammoth Dome, a group of solution cavities which H. C. Hovey estimated to be 400 feet long, 150 feet wide, and 250 feet in maximum height.

Mammoth Cave has many neighbors which, although less widely known, are no less interesting. Some of these are in places adorned with furnishings of onyx marble. One of the most impressive of the adornments in this group of caves is that known as Frozen Niagara (Plate XLIII), a mass of cave marble about 60 feet high.

Carlsbad Cavern

The most impressive of American caverns, the Carlsbad Cavern, in southeastern New Mexico, has only recently come prominently into notice. Long known locally, its unusual nature was disclosed to the readers of the National Geographic Magazine in January, 1924. Later in the same year the National Geographic Society sent an expedition under the leadership of the writer of this account to explore and study the cavern. The results were announced in the magazine in September, 1925.

Carlsbad Cavern has nothing to do with Carlsbad in central Europe. It is in southeastern New Mexico, in the foothills of the Guadalupe Mountains. The astonishing nature of this cavern was discovered by examinations made of proposed sites of reservoirs on Pecos River. The rocks that cause the reservoirs to leak contain the great cavern.

The first work of the explorers of this cave was done on the trail. Rough places were smoothed out and improvements were made that enabled us to reach the starting place of our work in little more than an hour's time, instead of two hours, as before. The chambers previously explored were used as points of departure for new discoveries. From them we pushed our way into the unknown parts.

We emulated Tom Sawyer in the use of kite strings. We used stretches of white twine, which were left as permanent markers. In time we had laid out a system of avenues marked with white twine that led to the exit.

Allow me now to take you on a personally conducted tour through this new wonderland. It must be a flying trip, for it would take days to examine all the strange features.

The cavern is approached from Carlsbad over a plain and up a mountain side to an opening where the roof collapsed. Near this opening a shaft had been dug and fitted with a windlass and wire rope having an iron bucket at the end. We climb into this bucket, the floor at the top of the shaft opens, and we descend 170 feet into Stygian darkness. Those who enter in the future will miss the ride on this bucket elevator, for a stairway has now been built in the natural opening.

After spending a little time in adjusting the lanterns and in getting our "cave eyes" we take the trail, picking our way over and among great blocks of rock that have fallen from the ceiling. We pass into a great opening, climbing up and down and over and finding our way around blocks of rock that have fallen from the ceiling, which is 250 feet above us, so far above that the lanterns only dimly illuminate it.

Three quarters of a mile from the entrance and more than 800 feet under the surface of the ground we reach the roughest place on the trail. Here were found parts of a human skeleton. Some cave man had lost his way and perhaps fell from rock to rock in the darkness to the shelf where his earthly career ended.

The spectacular part of the cavern begins just beyond this difficult part of the trail.

The first chamber to be entered is what is called Shinav's Wigwam, for the names of the features of the Cavern have been taken from Indian mythology. This chamber is nearly circular in outline, 200 feet across, 75 feet high, and wonderfully adorned. At the entrance to this glorified wigwam of the Navajo's wolf god hangs a large stalactite of gnarled appearance, which resembles a cave man's war club.

Around the walls of the wigwam are alcoves and niches and tributary chambers of marvelous character and amazing adornment. Had the author of "The Arabian Nights" seen Carlsbad Cavern he might have enriched his tale of Aladdin and his lamp with facts stranger than his fictions.

One of the most beautiful of these tributary chambers was discovered by an explorer who crept through a small hole in the wall of the Wigwam. Beyond the thin partition in which he found this hole a surprisingly spectacular view never before seen by human eye met his astonished gaze.

The new chamber thus discovered was named Avanyu's Retreat, for the wise serpent of Indian mythology, who is said to have lived in the waters of the underworld and who insisted on attending the councils of the gods.

We must not linger long in the Wigwam, for the most spectacular part of the cavern lies beyond. To reach it we climb over a pile of rocks 183 feet high, heaped on the floor of an enormous vault whose ceiling rises 350 feet above the floor. The inner slope of this hill leads down through a decorated archway into the Big Room, a great cavity half a mile long surrounded by tributary chambers and corridors, alcoves and niches.

These tributary avenues were searched in the hope of finding an exit through which an easy entrance to the cavern might be constructed. The search led to many new discoveries — too many to be even mentioned here.

Some of the most interesting discoveries were made in the basement of the cavern. A series of chambers was found 90 feet below the floor of the Big Room. The guide was lowered first on a rope through a hole in the floor. In the uncertain light of his kerosene torch, what he saw looked strange and unreal. All went well, however, until he reached water at the bottom of the hole. To his perturbed mind this seemed like an ocean. His frantic signals to be raised were misunderstood, and he was dropped unceremoniously into what proved to be a fountain. With his light gone, he passed an unhappy moment in the darkness before he discovered that he could touch bottom.

Later a wire ladder 90 feet long was built and lowered into the hole. The lower 75 feet of the ladder swung clear of the wall. A wire ladder thus suspended has an erratic disposition and an obstinate nature. Those who first descended were swayed and spun about in the darkness, and some whose nerves were weak had a sorry time.

The newly discovered chambers are extensive and wonderfully decorated. It is quite impossible to describe them. The only way to realize their marvels is to see them.

Carlsbad Cavern is believed to be the most spectacular underground wonderland in America, if not in the whole world. However, it may be excelled by some unexplored caverns in the Guadalupe Mountains.

For spacious chambers and for variety and striking beauty of decoration, Carlsbad Cavern is king of its kind.

The observer finds here many a stalagmite of impressive proportions and many a stalactite hanging gracefully from the decorated ceiling. The titanic proportions of some of the formations of cave marble, the grace and beauty of others, and the weird appearance of still others, suggesting gnomes and fairies and unearthly scenes, all combine to make the cavern a place of wonder, impressive and unforgetable.

Carlsbad Cavern is the work of water. Like many another well-known cave, it was made by the solution and removal of parts of the rocks. It differs from others in that the limestone

PLATE XXXIV, A. "THE CORYPHODON WAS HORRIFIED."

A restoration by Charles R. Knight of *Coryphodon testes,* a short-toed hoofed mammal whose fossil remains are found in rocks of Eocene age in Wyoming. By permission of the American Museum of Natural History.

PLATE XXXIV, B. THE MAMMOTH, A RESTORATION BY CHARLES R. KNIGHT.

Elephants of this kind ranged widely through the northern countries so recently that they are supposed to be contemporaneous with primitive man By permission of the American Museum of Natural History.

Plate XXXV. Iceberg Lake, in Glacier National Park.

Showing a cirque with glacial ice and a small lake at the bottom. Blocks of ice broken from the edge of the glacier float in the water like icebergs in the sea, even in midsummer. Photograph taken Aug. 13, 1911, by M. R. Campbell.

rocks here contain beds of gypsum and rock salt. Here through long ages the underground water dissolved and carried away soluble material, leaving a great cavity deep down under the highlands.

In the course of time, after the cavities were formed, the process was reversed and parts of the carbonate of lime were deposited from solution in forms commonly called flowstone and dripstone. Thus were formed the decorations of cave marble.

Many a description of caverns emphasizes their great antiquity. We are likely to regard them as the dwelling places of cave men and to think of them in connection with the infancy of the human race, which, in comparison with the lifetime of a man, was long, long ago. But in terms of earth history the advent of the human race is a very recent event. Caverns may have been in existence long ages before the first men entered them and may yet be geologically very young.

The youth of a cavern considered from a geologist's point of view and the antiquity of the same cavern considered from the ordinary human standpoint are illustrated by a cavern in western New Mexico that was found in beds of recent lava. Geologically this cavern is very young; yet it contains the remains of prehistoric people.

As this is one of the most conspicuous ice caves yet discovered, the original description of it is repeated here.

AN ICE CAVE IN NEW MEXICO[1]

New Mexico is a land of natural wonders. To such features as the beautifully symmetrical crater cone of Mount Capulin and the spectacular Carlsbad Cavern, set aside as national monuments, is now added a new curiosity in the form of an unusually interesting ice cave.

The cave is situated in the western part of the State, about fifty

[1] Reprinted from the *Geographical Review*, Vol. 16, 1926, pp. 55-59, published by the American Geographical Society of New York.

miles southeast of Gallup and an equal distance from Grants. It is readily reached by automobile from either town. The writer's party made the visit from Gallup. Leaving that coal-mining town early one morning, we motored southward through the Zuni Indian Reservation to the Mormon town of Ramah.

A few miles farther east the ruins of some ancient cliff dwellings were visited. Little is known of the ruins in this part of New Mexico, but their number suggests that this country once supported a much greater population than it does at the present time. A stop was also made at Inscription Rock, now known as the El Morro National Monument, where the face of the massive sandstone is covered with inscriptions dating back to the early Spanish expeditions.

The Lava Country

Another run of half an hour brought us to the foot of a great volcanic cone, once used as a signal station and known locally as Cerro de la Bandera, or Flag Butte. The cone rises steeply many hundreds of feet above the plain on which it stands. Its summit has an altitude of 8300 feet according to our aneroid. The slope of loose volcanic cinders is as steep as unconsolidated material will lie. The lower part is covered with pine trees; the upper part is nearly barren. The great crater depression in the top of the cone was estimated as about 500 feet deep. The rim is broken away on one side as if the last flow of lava had broken through and carried away the material of the rim.

Cerro de la Bandera stands at the northern margin of a great lava field — rough, black *malpais* (bad country) — that stretches away as far as the eye can reach. It is known as Los Veteados, or the veined country, because of great cracks formed when the lava cooled. Many of these "veins" or cracks lead down into hollows where the molten lava escaped during the closing stages of flow, leaving the solidified crust arching over caves. These caves have long been used as places of refuge. Many a criminal has escaped capture by retiring to some such refuge in the *malpais*, where pursuit is practically impossible by those who are not intimately acquainted with the devious passages. The Apache warriors were wont to leave their women and children in these natural shelters when they went on the warpath or set out on foraging expeditions. Judging from the numerous rock shelters and fragments of pottery of ancient design, the custom was a very ancient one.

Features of the Ice Cave

The ice cave, which was our objective, is no exception to the rule. Evidences of former occupation were found on all sides of it. Doubtless this was a favorite refuge, because within the cave is a permanent supply of good drinking water.

The cave is located on the side from which the crater rim was carried away and is so situated that it is best examined in the morning light. It is about 50 feet below the surface and opens into a large depression formed by the collapse of the roof. Apparently the last flow of lava from the crater, perhaps the one that broke through the rim, was 50 to 75 feet deep. Where the cave is situated the lava crusted over to a depth of 50 feet or more, when the rock below, still in a fluid state, flowed out, leaving a long, irregularly shaped hollow. The crust above this cave collapsed in several places, but in other places it remains arched over the hollow. The largest depression thus formed is the entrance to the ice cave.

We clambered down the wall of jagged rocks into the large opening, made our way over the angular blocks of fallen rock that once formed the roof, and finally entered the dark cavern, where artificial light was needed. There we saw before us a perpendicular wall of clear blue ice extending entirely across the cave, a distance of about 50 feet, and rising 14 feet above the floor. Other visitors had been there before us, bringing with them the trunk of a small pine tree which served as a rude ladder. By means of it we climbed to the top of the ice.

The upper surface of the ice is level for about 30 feet back from the face and then gradually slopes inward toward the back of the cave. The total thickness of the ice is not known, for the bottom is nowhere exposed. Most of the ice is clear and has a bluish tint. It lies in horizontal layers separated by thin seams of impure ice. At one horizon near the top are several large blocks of rock, apparently fallen from the ceiling and later covered.

We took the temperature at several places in the ice cave. It was a warm day in August. The water standing in the pool at the base of the wall of ice, the air above the ice and in the cave back of the main mass, and the rock of the inner walls all showed a temperature of 32° F.

The effect of the summer heat is seen near the mouth of the cave.

The ice is so far from the opening that the rays of sun never strike it; but a warm current of air occasionally reaches it. The winds at the surface cause shifting of air currents in the sink and to a less extent in the cave itself. The net result of the summer activity of the warm currents is shown in the form of the ice where the face is curved, suggesting swirling currents of warm air.

Origin of the Ice

The occurrence of perpetual ice in large quantity in caves is rare, although many small bodies of ice are known. Edwin Swift Balch describes a large number of such bodies in a volume on "Glacières or Freezing Caverns" (1900), and a recent publication by Georg Kyrle, "Grundriss de theoretischen Speläologie," contains additional information. Also many ice caves in the lava fields of the Northwest have been examined but not described in print. None, however, that have come to the writer's notice excel that at Cerro de la Bandera in volume of ice.

The occurrence of ice formed in caves has given rise to much speculation and in some instances to wild conjecture. However, one need not look for extraordinary causes in explanation of the ice, nor is it necessary to appeal to chemical changes, exhalations of gas, or other rare phenomena. The ordinary changes in weather and the well-known characteristics of scoriaceous basalt appear to be quite sufficient to account for the ice in our ice cave, though no extended observations were made in it.

At the altitude of this cave, 7300 feet or more above sea level, the cold of winter is severe, and freezing weather lasts many months. During times of frost the cold air circulates among the rocks, cooling them below the freezing temperature. Water flowing into the cooled spaces congeals. During thawing weather warm air circulates through the open spaces and warms the rocks. If, on the whole, the warmth prevails, as it does in most places, the ice of winter melts in summer, and there is no perpetual supply. But in a few favored places the summer heat does not overcome the winter frost, and the ice formed during the cold season is not entirely melted during the warm season. In brief, there is a lagging of effect in the change of temperature. The "cold" of winter is conserved in the cave just as it is in an ice house. It is even possible that the temperature of the rocks to a considerable depth beneath the surface

Plate XXXVI. Yosemite Valley, California, as Seen from an Airplane.

A typical ice-sculptured gorge, showing at the left the granite face of El Capitan, which rises about 3,000 feet above the bottom of the famous gorge and, at the right, the pinnacle of Sentinel Rock and the well-known form of Half Dome. Photograph by U. S. Army Air Service.

PLATE XXXVII. LOOKING A MOUNTAIN IN THE FACE. THE NORTH SLOPE OF MOUNT HOOD, OREGON, AS SEEN FROM AN AIRPLANE, SHOWING SEVERAL OF THE MOUNTAIN GLACIERS.

Official photograph by U. S. Army Air Service.

may be lowered so far below the freezing point during a long cold period that freezing may continue after all ice has melted from the surface. The accumulation of ice in spring and early summer has been noted in several places. Its formation in the Decorah Ice Cave, in Iowa, has been described by Alois F. Kovarik.[1]

Scientific Interest

It may not be out of place to call attention to the possibility of making scientific observations here of a timely nature. The lava in which this cave is situated results from a relatively recent volcanic eruption — how recent is not known. The liquefied rock flooded the lowland east of the Zuñi Mountains and flowed northward to the San José River at Grants, where the congealed lava, as seen from the railway, appears quite fresh.

This is one of the lava flows said to be so recent that it might have taken place in historic time. Yet on this flow stand large pine trees, and in it is a cave with a body of ice of such nature that it must represent accumulation through many years. Also on the lava near the cave are the remains of a prehistoric people.

The banding of the ice in the cave suggests a possibility of working out a chronology. The mass is made up of layers of ice. Each layer may represent a year's accumulation or it may represent a climatic cycle. This could probably be determined by careful observation. It is not impossible that the climatic changes recorded in the ice might supplement the chronology obtained by studying the growth of trees. The large pine trees of this region offer an attractive start for such a comparison.

Basis of Geologic Time Division

As nearly all the land forms with which we are familiar were fashioned almost exclusively in the Quaternary period, it would be interesting to know what events brought the Tertiary period to a close and ushered in the Quaternary. An understanding of

[1] A. F. Kovarik: The Decorah Ice Cave and Its Explanation, *Scientific American Suppl.*, Vol. 46, 1898, November 26, pp. 19158–19159.

the subdivisions of rocks into systems and of geologic time into periods is necessary before this interest may be satisfied.

Sedimentary rocks were originally subdivided into systems because of physical differences. Later, when comparisons, which geologists call correlations, were made between rocks at widely separated localities, the fossils they contained were used as a means of correlation, sometimes to the exclusion of all other means.

Recently, however, a greater use of correlation by physical criteria has been advocated, and what is called diastrophism has been suggested as a basis for correlation. Diastrophism is a term used to denote such physical changes as upheaval and warping of the surface of the earth and the consequent shifting of seas. These physical changes are recorded in rock structure. Hence it is necessary to examine this structure in order to read earth history.

In reading earth history, as in reading other histories, we desire to know dates and lengths of periods. Some of the methods of estimating geologic time have already been stated, as well as some of the uncertainties in the conclusions. Other methods employed deal with glacial and post-glacial phenomena. The most widely known of these methods is the one employed by Taylor[1] and others in computing the time that has elapsed since the last continental ice sheet retreated from Niagara. They reckon time by the rate at which the river wears away the rocks.

The old gorge was filled with rock débris when the ice moved over it. When the glacier retreated northward a new gorge was started. The falls are retreating upstream at a rate that has been determined by careful measurement. From this rate and the length of the gorge the time required for their erosion may be computed.

Another method of measuring the time that has elapsed since

[1] Taylor F. B., Niagara Falls Folio, U. S. Geological Survey, Folio 190, 1913.

the ice retreated is based on a study of the varve clays of De Geer,[1] the laminated clays laid down near the retreating front of the glacial ice. The number of laminæ, or thin layers, indicate the age of the deposit in much the same way that the thin layers of silt in Egypt indicate the age of the Nile delta.

These and all other methods of measuring geologic periods in terms of years give only approximate results. No method has yet been devised for measuring accurately even the last and shortest period. Nor is there uniformity of opinion as to what event shall mark the end of one period and the beginning of another. In geologic history, as in human history, there is a constant march of events, so that a "period" is only a term invented for convenience.

Geologists have found it difficult to establish a foundation, one based either on structure or on fossils, which is generally satisfactory for distinguishing Tertiary from Quaternary events. Some have maintained that there is no adequate means of separation. Others have maintained that a change of conditions that allowed ice to accumulate in continent-wide sheets was sufficient reason for introducing a new period name. This question may be left to the professional geologist.

However, it may be of interest to those who would understand modern landscapes to know that the Rocky Mountain region was elevated in early Quaternary time and that the carving of these elevated lands by erosion produced most of the scenic features which make the West famous.

The material removed from the highlands by erosion was spread out over the lowlands and in it were entombed the remains of the creatures of that time. From the fossil bones found we have learned something of the character of the animals that lived in the West while the northern lands were covered with ice.

[1] DeGeer, Gerard, A Geochronology of the Last 12,000 years, *Cong. Int. Geol., Compte Rendu*, 1910, XI, pp. 241–253, 1912.

Among those living in southern Arizona at that time were large mastodons, camels, several kinds of horses, antelopes, deer, wolves, hyenas, tigers, and a great variety of smaller animals. Turkeys and many other kinds of birds were numerous. Among the turtles were some with shells five or six feet across. All of these beings, although they are here called by common names, belonged to species now extinct, and among them were creatures that have gone completely out of fashion. They have no known descendants. One of the strangest of these extinct forms is called *Glyptodon.* It was an armored animal something like the modern armadillo, with body armor or shell about five feet long and three feet wide.

In other parts of the country events entirely different in nature from those that affected the mountains were transpiring. While the Colorado was vigorously carving out the Grand Canyon, continental glaciers were forming in the more northerly parts of the country. Enormous sheets of ice, probably thousands of feet thick, covered large parts of North America as well as of Europe and Asia.

The occurrence of these vast quantities of ice in high latitudes — glacial ice like that which now envelops all of Greenland except its marginal parts — indicates that the Quaternary was a wintry age. Why the relatively mild climate of the preceding age should have changed to a world-wide winter is a mystery. This change was probably not sudden, nor was it necessarily very great; perhaps the average annual temperature was lowered only a few degrees. All that is necessary for the formation of a glacier is that more snow shall fall than is melted.

More of the events of the Quaternary period have been worked out for the glaciated regions than for other parts of the country. Hence, in order to know what was going on elsewhere while the canyons of the Colorado were being cut and while the mountains were being carved out, we must turn to the story we find in the more northerly regions. In North America there were three main centers of accumulation of this glacial ice. These were in Canada. Farther south there were numerous local centers on mountains or on other high lands. Some local glaciers were formed as far south as Arizona.

Great Ice Age

During the glacial epoch the ice from the northern lands spread southward and covered large parts of North America. In moving over the land it picked up soil and fragments of rock and carried them long distances. When the ice melted it laid down its load of rock waste in deposits called glacial till, which now forms the unassorted masses of clay, pebbles, and boulders seen in river bluffs and road cuts in glaciated regions.

The first stage of glaciation closed with the melting of the ice and the beginning of a warm interglacial time. A remarkable assemblage of animals invaded the glaciated region after the first ice had disappeared, and the bones of many of them have been found in the interglacial deposits. The remains of horses, camels, stags, elephants, mastodons, mammoths, and sloths have been identified. During the life of these animals the climate of North America was rather mild and vegetation was abundant. After this mild interglacial stage, ice again spread southward and invaded the northern part of the United States. This second stage of glaciation was followed by other warm interglacial stages and by later advances of the ice.

It should not be inferred from this rapid review that the events here related were unimportant or that the glacial epoch was short. The duration of the Great Ice Age, although short as reckoned in geologic time, must be measured in hundreds of thousands of years.

Animals of the Great Ice Age

The creatures of the Great Ice Age are particularly interesting because they are nearer to us in time than those of earlier periods and therefore more nearly like animals now living; yet many that lived in North America during this age were very different from those living here today. To find the descendants or near relatives of the Pleistocene animals of North America we must go to other continents, for some of them as far as India. They may have been scattered by the changes in climate which caused the repeated advance and retreat of continental ice sheets during the Great Ice Age.

The animals of early Pleistocene time were of various kinds. They were adapted to the mild climate which then prevailed, and they remained until the ice advanced southward. But they were driven away or exterminated before the end of the Ice Age, and their places were taken by animals such as are now found only in the frozen North. When the ice finally melted away and the climate became as mild as it is now, these arctic species followed the retreating ice front northward, and their places were taken by animals adapted to a temperate climate.

If a Pleistocene man could return and view the present day animals, some of these might seem as strange to him as those of the African jungle seem to an inhabitant of the Great Plains. The Pleistocene horses had a modern appearance; also many of the deer, bison, and smaller animals. But for some of the forms that were common in Pleistocene time — such as the mastodon, the woolly rhinoceros, the saber-tooth tiger, and the camels — the Pleistocene visitor would look in vain. They left no descendants in North America, and their nearest relatives can be found now only in far distant lands.

Most surprising, as well as most common in the North American landscape, is the presence of elephants and mastodons

(Plate XXXIV, A). They ranged widely over the continent, and in great numbers. Among the most interesting of these curious giants is the Siberian mammoth, which probably came into North America across "Bering Land" when some parts of Bering Sea were above water. Along the same route from Asia to North America may have come primitive man, perhaps at the same time that the mammoths came.

Scarcely less strange in an American landscape are the woolly rhinoceros, the tapir, the camel, the llama, and other animals which now have no representatives on the continent. One of the camels was a peculiar creature with very long legs and neck, resembling a modern giraffe. Other grotesque figures of the time were giant ground-sloths with enormous claws, which were probably used to drag down branches of trees and to dig roots.

Fossil remains of land animals are not so likely to be preserved as those of water animals; yet great numbers of them have been discovered. Many have been found in ancient bogs, where the animals were mired; others have been found in caverns, where carnivorous animals made their lairs and to which they dragged their prey.

A curious and effectual trap for ancient as well as modern animals is a so-called tar pit or asphalt lake in California. Here many a heavy animal, such as an elephant, venturing forth in search of food or water, was mired in the soft tar and perished. Skulking wolves in search of food approached the carcass or were driven by some stronger enemy into the tar. From this asphalt deposit, which is at Rancho LaBrea, near Los Angeles, the skeletons of many animals have been obtained, especially bison, ground-sloths, extinct horses, camels, mastodons, mammoths, bears, and gigantic extinct lions, as well as those of many kinds of birds.

The asphalt here accumulated around oil springs. As the oil came to the surface and evaporated it left a sticky residue of semi-liquid asphalt, which gradually hardened except where the oil continually welled up from below. A film of dust covered the asphalt, and water accumulated in the hollows after rain. Animals came to drink and, attempting to cross, were caught in the tenacious asphalt as in quicksand. Thus caught, they lured beasts and birds of prey, and they in turn, coming near to devour the unfortunate victims, were caught in the soft, sticky asphalt and in turn served to attract still others.

After the mammoth, the saber-toothed tiger has probably appealed more strongly to the imagination than any other of the monsters associated with early man. It was the largest of the cat family— about as large as a modern grizzly bear. It had long, flattened saber-like tusks, which projected about seven inches from their sockets and which it probably used for stabbing its victims. With such weapons of offense, Saber-tooth was probably able to prey upon very large animals, even mastodons and giant sloths. Although these great tigers were so modern as to be contemporaries of early man, they have left no descendants. Their race has become wholly extinct.

But Quaternary history in the West is not written more plainly in its fossils than in its gorges, canyons, cliffs, and mesas. The records are written large in the land forms. In the landscapes are written the episodes of recent geologic history. The best of these stories in stone may be read in the national parks.

Recent Epoch

Some things seen near at hand seem larger and more impressive than similar things seen from a distance.

Recent events are likely to crowd from the mind larger events of ancient history. In these respects geology offers no exception to the rule. The earth processes of the present time — that is, of the epoch known as Recent — probably receive more consideration than those of all former epochs combined.

PLATE XXXVIII. THE TERRACED FACE OF THE HOT SPRINGS DEPOSITS IN YELLOWSTONE PARK, OVERLOOKING THE TOURIST CAMP.

More than 154,000 people viewed this scene during the summer of 1925. Photograph by Willis T. Lee.

Plate XXXIX. Stalactites and Stalagmites in Carlsbad Cavern, New Mexico.

Scene in the Big Room, hundreds of feet underground, to which no ray of light other than that from the explorer's lantern ever penetrates. This cavern is noted for natural decorations of great variety and beauty, ranging from delicate forms of spatterstone to pillars of titanic proportions. Photograph by Ray V. Davis.

A systematic summary of the events of the Recent epoch — the Age of Man — would require much space. But as no pretence at completeness is made here we may pass over it lightly. This seeming neglect of recent geologic events may not appear unwarranted if we reflect that we are dealing chiefly with things that are not usually emphasized in works on geology. The natural processes that affect our comfort and happiness receive almost daily consideration. Much of this consideration comes under the heading of geography, a subject that is growing ever more popular. This popularity is well illustrated by the National Geographic Magazine, which within a period of about 35 years has reached a circulation of more than a million copies.

Much of our modern economic activity is dependent directly on geologic and geographic knowledge. Without that knowledge little of the billion or more barrels of oil used last year would have been produced; nor would the billion and a quarter tons of coal mined during that year have been available for driving trains across the continent and steamers around the world. But while the activities of the present time rightly command most of our attention, the geologist is ever mindful that modern conditions are only the natural results of processes that have been in operation continuously through past ages.

From the point of view of the geologist there is little distinction between the Great Ice Age and the Recent epoch, the Age of Man. The former ended in the United States when the last continental glacier, in its retreat northward about 35,000 years ago, abandoned the United States. But in Greenland, where an area of more than 500,000 square miles is covered thickly with ice, the Great Ice Age is not yet closed.

It is often said that geography is geology in the making. In this sense the geology of the Recent epoch is read in the physical geography of our time. It appears in the modern landscape, in the operating mine, and in the flowing well. Wind and frost, rain and river, the surging sea and all its straits and inlets are day by day making the geology of the future.

Now, as in all past time, the earth processes are building up masses of rock in some places and tearing down masses of rock in other places. The destructive process may be illustrated by a picture of Crater Lake, in Oregon, where sometime in the past a great mass of volcanic rock was heaped up. This mass is now being attacked by rain and frost and wind, and from it is being carved a landscape of great interest and beauty, shown in Plate XLIV.

Although most modern landscapes are the results of earth processes that reach far back in geologic time, the forms that lie immediately beneath the eye today were produced by erosion during the Recent epoch. The great mountain range in the landscape pictured opposite page 177 (Plate XLV) dates from some ancient time, and the dark volcanic cone in the middle ground was probably formed long before the beginning of Quaternary time. Yet the sculpturing of the mountain and the leveling of the plain, now covered with sage brush, was accomplished in very recent geologic time.

And so, in closing our rambling journey through the West, I would emphasize the fact that

> To him who in the love of Nature holds
> Communion with her visible forms, she speaks
> A various language,

and invite you to learn the language of Nature and to read in mountain and canyon, in river and lake, in the fossils and in the rocks, those Stories in Stone which tell the romance of our world.

CHAPTER X

A NEW METHOD OF OBSERVATION

AN interesting account might be written of the methods of obtaining geologic and geographic information. The geologist goes into every available nook and cranny of the earth, with eyes open and mind alert, to note each object of interest and to mentally grasp every significant relationship. He explores hill and plain, river and lake, bay and ocean. He descends into mines and caves; he traverses canyons and climbs mountains. Where he cannot go, he sends self-recording instruments. By bucket and cable he sends these instruments to the bottom of deep wells, and by balloons he sends them high in the air to altitudes greater than those of the highest mountain peaks.

The manner of his going is as varied as his methods of travel, for he uses every available means of transportation. He travels on foot and on horseback, by steamship and canoe, by camel, caravan, and dog team, and even by airplane.

Many a book has been filled from cover to cover with tales of travel, and many another has been devoted to descriptions of the methods and results of scientific observation. It is useless to attempt even the most condensed account of methods of geologic exploration in the space here at my disposal, and for this reason I shall confine my attention to the newest method of travel — that by means of aircraft.

Near the close of the World War I was engaged in geologic and geographic work along the Atlantic coast. Much of the area that I wished to examine is marsh land. Examination of it on the ground was slow, laborious, and generally unsatisfactory.

It seemed to me that some of the information desired as to the character of the surface could be obtained by observation from airplanes and by the use of cameras adapted to taking views of the land from high in the air.

In order to test this method of observation I spent about a year making flights in airplanes and in hydroplanes, collecting photographs taken from the air, and studying the character of the surface, both by observation from the air and by the inspection of these photographs. This work was made possible by a co-operative arrangement between the United States Geological Survey and the Army and Navy air services. The Army Air Service placed airplanes at my disposal at Bolling Field in Washington, D. C., at Langley Field in eastern Virginia, and at Mineola on Long Island. The Navy Air Service gave me similar privileges at Washington and at Rockaway, Long Island.

What is it like to mount high in the air and look down on the surface of the earth as one bends over a map spread out on a table? We hear conflicting stories of the sensations experienced by those who have taken trips in airplanes. Let me digress for a moment and tell you of one of my first flights, made from the aviation field at Mineola.

An Experience in the Air

The morning selected for the ascent was fair, but clouds that hung low on the horizon looked threatening. I had spent the night at the Officers' Club in order to lose no time in reaching the field in the morning, for we were to hop off as soon as the light was strong enough to permit us to take photographs.

We scanned the weather chart, noted the velocity and direction of the wind, and reached the decision that the storm promised by the weather man need not delay our trip in the air. But we lost some time in getting into flying togs and in warming up the motor.

PLATE XL. HEART OF THE BIG ROOM, CARLSBAD CAVERN, NEW MEXICO.

An illustration of the intensive decoration of this cavern. Floor, ceiling, and walls are completely covered with cave marble in infinite variety of form. For size, note the people standing in the center of the scene. Photograph by Willis T. Lee. Courtesy of the National Geographic Society.

PLATE XLI. A CHAMBER IN MAMMOTH CAVE.

Limestone walls and saltpeter vats in Booth's Theater. The nitrate-bearing earth, which had accumulated through long ages on the floor of the cave, was here leached out for the manufacture of gunpowder in 1812. Photograph by Willis T. Lee.

The biplane that carried me on this, my first, air journey was called Sky Pilot. I smiled at the name painted in large letters on the body of the plane, but on second thought that name did not seem wholly humorous. I was willing to be piloted away from earth for a little time but not permanently. I think I should have felt more comfortable had the biplane carried a less suggestive name.

I looked the machine over with critical eye. It had an awkward appearance. Like an eagle, which appears awkward and unattractive while on the ground, a biplane in repose can scarcely be called a thing of beauty. But when, like the eagle, it leaves the ground and rises easily and gracefully into the air it becomes an object of fascinating interest.

As we take off, we give little attention to appearances. Who cares for looks when deeds are all important! Onlookers may admire if they so desire; or they may smile at us if they please. Just now things of much greater import demand attention.

During the delay the clouds have approached, and even as we leave the ground the vapory forerunners of the storm are scudding past. We carefully adjust our goggles, for no unprotected eye can endure the blast of an airplane propeller, and take off, heading into the wind. For several moments we rise on a straight course in order to gain altitude. This course brings us close to a bank of heavy clouds. The dark masses look ominous as they threaten to engulf us. But our mechanical bird ignores the threat, wings its unobstructed way between two dark masses of vapor, and rises into a clear, brilliantly sunlit space above the clouds.

How different now!

A moment ago cloudy troubles darkened our sky; the silver linings seemed thin and lacked comfort, but now we gaze down on white, billowy masses that glow brilliantly in the sunlight. From above we can see nothing of the cloud except the silver lining.

As Sky Pilot mounts higher into the clear space the cloud that had threatened us for the moment seems to shrink and lose its impressiveness, and my attention suddenly returns to earth. But where is the flying field we left a few moments ago? I can not distinguish it. And what is that great, even surface that stretches endlessly beyond the reach of vision? I try to ask the pilot, but the roar of the engine is so deafening that no sound produced by human voice can be heard. Instead of words coming from my opened mouth a blast of air from the propeller goes into it and expands my cheeks like those of a puff adder. An airplane is an excellent place in which to learn to keep one's mouth shut. I have certain acquaintances who might take trips in the air frequently, with profit to themselves and others.

But sign language can be used, and, as if in answer to my bewildered look, the pilot makes a sign indicating waves of infinite number. Then I understand that I am gazing out over the Atlantic Ocean. Hastily I look down for dear old terra firma. I like water, but not too much at one time! I am not an expert swimmer!

But my faith in good old Sky Pilot is unshaken. There is no danger of falling into the water. Yet, some time ago — but of course there is no danger now! Oh! no. Nothing can happen today — but some time ago, something did happen and an airplane fell. I reflect that perhaps one might alight in water more easily than on land, for in most places land is hard. I signal to the pilot that the waves are very interesting — oh, very! — but there is no variety of scenery. They look much alike to me, and I have already seen enough of them. Things on land are more varied and in every way more interesting.

But where is the land? I look over one side of the airship and see only waves; then over the other side and see only blue, limitless sky. After a startled moment, I understand that in making the turn, the plane banked or tilted. My pleasure in this matter had not been consulted. But before I have opportunity to complain, good old Sky Pilot gracefully rights itself and recovers its former standing in my estimation, as sky and earth again appear in the relation that I have always assumed was proper for them.

The pilot now points to a white strip of land which stretches uninterruptedly as far as eye can reach. It slowly dawns on me that beach sand is white and that there are considerable quantities of it on the south shore of Long Island. The white strip is the sandy beach, on which the surf is breaking in white foam.

We now fly westward over the beach. Here lies Rockaway beneath us, and there is Coney Island. But these places look like little toy towns, composed of play houses. Toy boats appear out at sea — ocean greyhounds from over the water coming into New York Harbor. Other toy boats are leaving the harbor, destined for the ends of the earth.

To our right are cities and towns, orchards, and cultivated fields. A wormlike object is creeping along a dark trail — the Express headed for New York. Small, dark specks looking like ants on a white pathway must be automobiles on the cement turnpike. But what is that light strip beyond the dark land? Is it possible? Yes, that must be water. It must be Long Island Sound. A minute speck on it from which trails a long black streamer of smoke is a steamboat, and the dark land beyond must be Connecticut.

In answer to a signaled inquiry the pilot points to the altimeter, which registers 8,000 feet. One who flies a mile and a half above the ground can see a long way. Yes, I am really looking across Long Island and over the Sound far away into Connecticut.

On we go — for go we must, if we would stay in the air. No signs forbidding loitering are needed along the airways. The rule is go on or go down. So, on we go!

Brooklyn now lies beneath us. Doubtless there are people on the streets, but we can see none. The minute moving dots we see are busses and street cars.

Objects now flash into view so rapidly that I become bewildered. East River, with its great bridges and with its ferry boats coming and going; the harbor, with great steamers churning up the mud as their powerful propellers force them here and there; the enormous skyscrapers — but hold! are they so enormous? As we look down upon them, one is scarcely distinguishable from another. Height is not gaged from above. A five-story building and a fifty-story building may look much alike.

Suddenly the pilot points to the clouds rolling in from the sea in dense masses and signals that we must return before the storm breaks.

Looking a Thunder Storm in the Face

Then I recall the storm promised by the weather man. As we head eastward toward the rolling mass of clouds my attention is riveted on the difficulties ahead. All the wonders beneath us are forgotten for the moment. In spite of reason, I find it impossible to suppress the feeling that we are about to smash head foremost into a mountainous mass of solid matter, as we approach the thunder cloud.

How one's thoughts race at such a moment! In a flash I have a plan all worked out and supported by unanswerable arguments: rather than plunge into that cloud, where we may collide with thunderbolts, it will be much better to fly over into New Jersey ahead of the storm and land in some lady's flower garden, or perhaps in a soft cabbage patch, even if I have to pay for the ruined cabbages.

However, the pilot shows no concern and does not consult my wishes. But he glances sharply through every rift in the clouds, and his practiced eye picks up familiar objects on the ground.

Suddenly Sky Pilot swerves, circles about for a moment, and dives through a break in the clouds like a bird of prey swoop-

PLATE XLII. A DOME IN MAMMOTH CAVE.

Cathedral Dome, about 60 feet in diameter and 200 feet high. This dome was formerly approached through Mammoth Cave proper but is now reached through the new opening to the cave. Photographed by Willis T. Lee.

Plate XLIII. Frozen Niagara. Decorations of Onyx Marble in the New Entrance to Mammoth Cave.

ing down upon its victim. Through this rift we pass suddenly from the dazzling brilliance of a perfectly clear sky to the somber shadows beneath the storm clouds and reach the landing field well ahead of the rain.

I have never told the pilot about my plan to visit New Jersey, nor of my willingness to compensate irate owners of ruined cabbages, but I have had the pleasure of assuring him that he gave me an experience that I can never forget. Never before, nor since, have I been so close to a thunder storm in action.

This adventure, novel as it seemed at the time, was by no means my only unusual experience. Adventures in the air are all novel, but as I grew accustomed to the unusual sensations my attention became fixed more completely on the things that I was there to see and on the consideration of methods for presenting the results of the observations.

Commercial and Scientific Uses of Airplanes

Many others are interested in the face of the earth as it is seen from the air, and many are devoting time and thought to the adaptation of the airplane to scientific study. I was obliged to abandon this work, but others are continuing it, and much has been done to adapt the airplane and the camera to use as instruments for mapping. Considerable has also been done toward the adaptation of the airplane to use as an instrument for prospecting. It has been used by those who make search over broad stretches of country for prospective oil fields. Planes have been used for this purpose in Canada, Central and South America, and elsewhere.

The value of this commercial use of airplanes depends on the fact that from the air we may obtain a broad view of an area or an object, unobstructed by other objects in the foreground. This fact suggests other uses. The employment of airplanes by sightseers has long been advocated, and in some measure they have been used for viewing landscapes. Thus far their use has been confined chiefly to professional air men. But since these pioneers have blazed the trail, that trail will be followed by multitudes, unless in this instance the ordinary trend of history is reversed. The possibility of viewing landscapes from the air and of studying them from any point of view is illustrated by many of the photographs reproduced in this volume.

As airplanes and the cameras used in them are among the newer instruments to be adapted to the mapping of the surface of the earth and to delineating its features, it seems appropriate to point out here some of the obvious advantages gained by the use of these instruments.

It is a well-known fact, that in viewing an object, the part of the object that is close to the observer seems more prominent than equally large parts at a greater distance. In order that all parts may be seen in proper proportion, the object must be viewed from some distance. The larger the object, the farther away must the observer be in order that its constituent parts may appear in proper proportion.

In viewing places from the ground great difficulty may be experienced in selecting the best point for observation. Much time is spent in the national parks selecting scenic points and building trails to them. By use of an airplane any desired point of view may be occupied easily. Furthermore, when the landscape is viewed from the ground there are often unattractive objects in the line of vision which interfere with the view desired. In an airplane we rise above all petty obstacles and reach a position from which our view is unobstructed.

The ability to choose one's viewpoint is useful in many ways. Geographic information obtained from photographs taken from airplanes has been of great value to the landscape architect whose duty it is to lay out city parks in artistic pattern and to the engineer engaged in city planning. The most detailed map of a given area may fail to show the location of some object which the mapmaker regarded as unworthy of notice but which is of great interest or importance to the user of the map. The camera is no respecter of objects. It depicts every object with equal faithfulness.

The Picture Map

When a picture is desired of an area too large to be photographed on a single film a composite picture is made, which some call a mosaic and others a picture map. A mosaic is made up of photographs taken at regular intervals of time by a camera carried over such an area in an airplane. The pictures are then corrected for distortion, difference in scale, and other imperfections, and fitted together to make a continuous picture map. Great difficulty is experienced in making the corrections, and although the mosaics serve many useful purposes the methods of making them have not yet been perfected to a stage where they may replace other kinds of maps. They have, however, reached a stage where maps made from the pictures supplemented by ground surveys are more accurate than maps made from ground surveys alone.

Mosaics have been made of many of the well-known parts of the country, such, for example, as Boston (including the harbor and surrounding land), New York and neighboring parts of Long Island and New Jersey, Chicago, San Francisco, and many other cities. Unfortunately, the picture maps are so large that they can not now be used as illustrations in books like this one.

Before me as I write is a picture map of an area of about 400 square miles in California, including Los Angeles. The map is about 5 feet square. Its scale is too small now to show distinctly objects much smaller than city blocks. A further reduction in size would obliterate much that is desired on such a map. It is to be hoped that ways may soon be found to publish such mosaics at a reasonable cost. They are too useful to lie in obscurity.

In viewing a landscape from the air one gets an impression of it similar to that obtained from a map of the country. My first impression of this kind is one never to be forgotten. I had been making observations in eastern Virginia for some time and was familiar with the geographic features as they appear from the ground and as they are represented on the map.

Then one day at Langley Field, the flying station north of Norfolk, Va., I stepped into an airplane and was lifted several thousand feet into the air, where I spent three hours looking at the country from this new point of view. The flight took me over Dismal Swamp and westward nearly to Richmond and northward to the Potomac River. Then we turned eastward to the shore of Chesapeake Bay and flew southward over the numerous streams, bays, and marshes of eastern Virginia. During the entire flight I gazed down on familiar scenes with a feeling that I was looking at a map. Every stream, town, and road was clearly visible and plainly recognizable.

Air Journeys Over Difficult Places

Observation from an airplane is particularly useful in areas difficult of access, such as marshes, swamps, and mud flats, and in tracts cut by streams and inlets into an intricate complex of land and water. Many of the marshes and mud flats in eastern Virginia are impassable and can be seen only from above.

Some parts of the West are equally impassable, but for a very different reason. There are badlands cut by deep, narrow arroyos. There are sun-parched deserts like that of Death Valley. There are precipitous walls which have never been scaled, like those of the Grand Canyon. But the flier soars over mud flat and mountain alike and looks down with the same equanimity upon unscalable wall and impenetrable marsh.

A peculiar advantage is gained by use of airplanes in mountainous districts. This advantage is obvious to anyone who has tried to illustrate mountain scenery by photographs or by other means. From such a distance that a large mountain appears in proper proportion all details may be lost. From nearby points we are likely to see only undesirable foreground. By use of an airplane we may select our point of view, look a mountain peak squarely in the face (Plate XXXIII), or gaze down into the very throat of a volcano, such as that shown in Plate III.

Much work has been done in constructing relief maps and plaster models, and in devising other means of representing mountainous areas, for the purpose of showing clearly the interrelations of mountain and plain and of ridges and canyons. Pictorial representations of these things can now be obtained from the objects themselves by means of air photography.

Seeing Things Under Water

An advantage of a still different nature is obtained along the seashore and in areas of shallow water. From a distance above the surface we are able to look down through a considerable body of water and to distinguish objects on the bottom. During the World War submarines were "spotted" and followed by observers in aircraft.

In the course of my airplane work along the Atlantic coast I found that I could see on the bottom not only such objects as sunken boats but submerged land forms like the terraces and sand banks off Pensacola, Fla. (Plate XLVIII), and the channels, both natural and dredged, in rivers like the Potomac (Plate XLIX). Little has been done toward adapting this method of observation to the study of geology and physical geography, but it seems to offer great possibilities of usefulness.

Another way in which the airplane may be found useful to the geologist is in the examination of rock formations and the search for bodies of minerals. I have no thought of suggesting that this method of observation will ever entirely supplant the slow, laborious methods of work on the ground, but there are many ways in which a rapid survey of an area made by flying over it may be useful.

Each kind of rock has recognizable characteristics. Some are red, others gray, and still others brown or black. Certain kinds of plants thrive on limestone and not on sandstone. Some rock formations weather into cliffs, others into broken surfaces, and still others into smooth level surfaces. These characteristics may be seen from high in the air and recognized from air photographs. Geologists of the American Expeditionary Forces in France during the World War were able to identify geologic formations from air photographs and after ascertaining the characteristics of these formations where the rocks could be examined they were able to map the same formations in areas behind the enemy's lines and so to point out favorable routes of march along which firm road beds might be found.

An intensely practical use of geology to fliers came to my attention some time ago. The geologic formations of England have long been studied, and a complete geologic map of the country has been made. Each kind of rock has a special color and habit of weathering. Certain types of trees and shrubs thrive on it which do not thrive on neighboring rocks of other kinds. Aviators who had studied the geology of England with a view to recognizing the surface from aloft found that, with a small geologic map before them, they were able to determine their location.

The official who developed this method of observation said that in flying across the Channel from the continent he often ascended to great altitudes to avoid unfavorable flying conditions, and was frequently above clouds which obscured the ground. On descending through the clouds somewhere over England he could first recognize by the general aspect of the country the geologic formation he was over. By reference to his geologic map he ascertained his approximate position. By the time he had approached the surface near enough to recognize towns and smaller objects he had headed in the general direction of his destination and was able to recognize the smaller objects which served as more exact guides.

Airplanes and Charts

There is probably no way in which an airplane is of greater use to the geologist than in making maps and charts. Since the great development of the airplane during the World War as an instrument for observation, methods of using it for making maps have been developed rapidly. From the many adaptations that might be mentioned, two may be selected as representative — the charting of coast lines and the mapping of such features of an area as fields, forests, towns, roads, and streams.

It is necessary for the safety of ships that coast lines be accurately charted, and that the charts be revised when changes take place in the relation of land and water. In many places the coast line may be notably shifted during a storm. In a large country like the United States, which has more than 52,000 miles of coast, the problem of maintaining up-to-date charts is difficult. Revision of a chart of the shore line where it has been changed can be made readily from airplane photographs.

The airplane has already abundantly proved its worth as an effective instrument for making maps, and new ways are being devised for still further increasing this kind of usefulness. It is quite impossible to describe in the limited space of this brief chapter the methods by which the results of observations from the air are transferred to paper in the making of a map. I must be content with the statement that the several mapmaking organizations have found that the use of the airplane has materially reduced the cost of mapping, hastened the process, and greatly increased the accuracy of the maps. In a recent report, the committee on photographic surveying of the Federal Board of Surveys and Maps states that an average saving of 25 per cent in the cost of its maps is made by the United States Geological Survey through the use of air photography.

The speeding of the output of the mapmakers is timely in view of a recent law that provides for the completion of the map of the United States within twenty years, although Congress has made no appropriation that will expedite the work now being done. In order to accomplish this task great speed would be necessary, for less than half the area of the United States, which includes more than 3,000,000 square miles, has been mapped in the way contemplated by the United States Geological Survey.

I may add that this committee states that in 1924 the Army Air Service supplied to the Geological Survey air photographs covering nearly 900 square miles for the purpose of making standard topographic maps, and that in 1925 photographs of 9,300 square miles were supplied for this purpose. For 1926 photographs have been requested for 36,000 square miles in the United States proper and for 20,000 square miles in Alaska.

Plate XLIV. Rain Erosion in Sand Canyon, Crater Lake National Park.

The needle-like pinnacles in the side of the canyon are remnants of recent erosion in the lava beds of an old volcano. Photograph by Fred Kiser. Courtesy National Park Service.

Plate XLV. View of the Eastern Face of the High Sierra, California, Showing a Great Fault Scarp and a Volcanic Cone at the Foot of the Scarp.

The floor of Owens Valley, shown in the foreground, consists of sand and gravel, which supports a sparse growth of desert vegetation, chiefly sagebrush. The buildings and trees in the middle distance mark the course of Owens River, which now supplies water for the City of Los Angeles. The great dark mass at the foot of the high mountains consists of igneous rock. The higher part of this mass is the cone of an extinct volcano, built up during a long succession of eruptions of molten lava, which issued from the vent in the center of the cone and spread over its flanks and to some extent over the floor of the valley. Photograph by Willis T. Lee.

Chapter XI

LEGENDS OF CREATION

If your patience is not already exhausted and you retain a determination to remain with me to the end, will you consider with me now some of the legends of the origin of the earth, and some of the ancient and modern beliefs concerning it.

Thus far we have been thinking in present-day terms and using modern expressions. But in geology, as in everything else, present conceptions and beliefs are the results of growth. Some one in the dim past, perhaps, had a crude, imperfect idea. Some other person following him saw a germ of truth in the idea and improved on it. Succeeding men perfected the idea, retaining the good and rejecting the bad. Thus did geology grow.

The growth of the science of geology might well be likened to the growth of a plant. A seed that does not look much like the mature plant but that has in it the germ of life, is planted and growth follows. The young plant may not look like the seed nor like the plant at later stages, but after going through a period of growth it finally blooms and produces fruit.

It has been said that if we could know all the circumstances that entered into the formation of a conception we would find no ground of criticism for those who hold that conception. It is quite impossible to know all the circumstances that gave rise to men's early conceptions and misconceptions of the earth's formation or even to discuss at length those which are well known, and yet I cannot resist the temptation of setting down some of those things in the history of the science that have interested me. I like to think of the science of geology as I would of a person whose biography I am considering.

No man's biography is complete unless it tells just where and when he was born. Even though the circumstances of his birth may have not the slightest bearing on his accomplishments, we feel unacquainted with him until we learn when and where his life began. As we proceed with his history we are conscious that the biographer is leaving out many things that might be said. He is dealing only with those events and circumstances which he deems important. Another biographer might handle the subject in a wholly different manner.

So in this account of the growth of the science of geology I shall set down only such things as have appealed to me as being interesting. In doing so I am fortunately able to begin with an event in which all are interested.

Everyone is interested in the mode of origin of the earth, and there are many different accounts of it. Some of these accounts harmonize with many facts; others with a few; and still others are wholly legendary. The savage may accept a myth which to us seems ludicrous; the less primitive man may credit a legend of uncertain origin; the credulous man may hold to a supposed revelation; and one scientist may entertain a theory which seems untenable to others.

Ancient Speculations

The present conceptions regarding the origin of the earth and its early history have arisen through a long period of mental development. The earliest explanations were vague and nebulous, but some had in them the possibilities of healthy growth.

Primitive men seem to have felt the necessity of explaining the things which they observed, especially the things that excited fear. They knew nothing of the cause of lightning and thunder, of chasms and mountains, of darkness and storm. And yet their "wise" men, the priests of old and the medicine men of the aborigines, in order to maintain their reputation for mental superiority, must give some convincing explanation of these things to those whom they presumed to instruct. (I wonder if "wise" men will ever outgrow this habit?) For this reason lightning was said to result from the bolts of Jove; chasms were formed as passage-ways for the gods; darkness and storm resulted from the wrath of some divinity.

Indian Myths

It is not difficult to imagine how myths and fables sprang up and how stories which appealed to the imagination gained credence. A belief once established and incorporated in the tradition of a race, although it may be as impossible as the Hindoo's Tortoise-theory of the earth, is likely to live as long as the race endures.

Edward B. Tylor, in his "Researches into the Early History of Mankind," states (p. 339) that: "In the Old World the Tortoise Myth belongs especially to India, and the idea is developed there in a variety of forms. The Tortoise that upholds the earth is called in Sanskrit *Kûrmaraja*, 'King of the Tortoises,' and it is said that the Hindoos believe to this day that the world rests upon its back. Sometimes the snake, Sesha, bears the world on its head, or an elephant carries it upon its back, and both snake and elephant are themselves supported by the great tortoise. The earth, rescued from the deluge which destroys mankind, is set up with the snake that bears it resting on the floating tortoise, and a deluge is again to pour over the face of the earth when the world-tortoise, sinking under its load, goes down into the great waters."

The creation myths of the aborigines assume the preëxistence of matter and of living beings, which differ from present beings chiefly in the possession of grotesque characteristics and supernatural powers. Such a being, for example, is the Alaskan Indians' Black Crow, which is represented as incubating a human mask, or the Iroquois' Great Hare, floating on his raft and causing other animals to dive and bring up a grain of sand, which becomes the continent.

Many of the Indian stories of creation are childish or fantastic, and in their setting reach little beyond the tepee and the hunting ground. The creator of the object whose explanation is sought is usually some animal or bird of supernatural power or some superhuman creature of impossible attributes. Many of the myths remind us of the stories which spring spontaneously from children in the game of "Tell-me-stories."

Some of the myths seem to justify the belief that in the American Indian we have an example of suspended race progress similar to arrested mental development in the individual. These Indians seem to show a lower mental plane than that shown by the oldest legends recorded in ancient history, although some of the oldest, as, for example, the Tortoise theory, seem little superior to the Indian myths. In others, such as the legend which states that "the self-existent lord with a thought created the waters and deposited in them a seed which became a golden egg, in which egg he himself is born as Brahma, the progenitor of the worlds," the grotesqueness is coupled with a conception of deity. Still others, such as a hymn in the Rig Veda (x. 129) which begins, "There then was neither Aught nor Naught," endeavor to reach back to a time when nothing existed and to seek to derive something from nothing.

As the myths of the American Indians appear to belong to an earlier stage of development than that which produced the Hindoo's theory of the earth they seem to be of very early origin. The beliefs underlying the legends embodied in the Rig Veda must have gained credence before that book was written and therefore before 1500 B.C.; hence the Hindoo beliefs, and perhaps also the American Indian's legends, seem to have been developed before the poetical conceptions of the early Greeks had crystal-

Plate XLVI. A Page from the Story of the Earth.

The language in which some of the Stories in Stone are written. These fossil shells from rocks of middle Tertiary age in eastern Virginia are the remains of clams and snails that lived in the shallow water of a Miocene sea. When the mollusks died their shells were buried in the silt on the sea bottom. In time this silt became stone.

Plate XLVII. An Ice Cave in Western New Mexico.

Looking back into the cavern over the top of the ice. The three persons in the foreground are standing at the foot of the ice wall, which is 50 feet long and 14 feet high. The man above is standing on the great mass of ice, which extends back 30 feet and then slopes gently downward toward the back of the cave. The irregular masses in the foreground are rocks from the collapsed roof. Photograph by Willis T. Lee.

lized into the hero-stories which every schoolboy is familiar with, and before the Babylonian accounts of creation had evolved into the still more dignified Mosaic account. The possibility of the ancient origin of the American Indian myths is strengthened by the evidence coming rapidly to light that the American continent has been inhabited from very ancient time.

An early story of creation is inscribed in cuneiform characters on tablets found in the ruins of Nineveh. The translation states that "Long ago, when the heavens above had not been named and the earth beneath had no name and only Apsu (the Ocean), the primeval, who begot them, and Tiamat, Confusion, who bore them both, existed . . . then were created all the gods." The story proceeds with a somewhat lengthy account of strife among the gods and the creation of lightning and storm for use in battle. One god finally triumphs over the others and proceeds to create the earth and sky.

On other tablets excavated at Nippur,[1] said to be older than 1200 B.C. and possibly written before 2000 B.C., the origin of the human race is described. A time before the existence of the earth is pictured; the creation of man, his misfortunes, his prosperity, and his rise to supremacy all are described.

Early Beliefs

The legends of the Greeks and other ancient peoples, as well as those of the modern aborigines, ascribed natural phenomena to their hero-gods. In the mind of the ancients it thundered when Thor threw his hammer, sunlight was the effulgence of the sun god, the storm at sea was caused by the wrath of Neptune, and the volcano resulted from the fire in the forge of Vulcan.

The ancient Hebrews in like manner ascribed all natural phenomena directly to their god, but as they acknowledged only

[1] Barton, G. A., Am. Philos. Soc. Proc., vol. 56, pp. 275–280, 1917.

one deity, they explained phenomena that were unfavorable to their happiness as due to his wrath, and those that were favorable to their happiness to his beneficence. Neither they nor their contemporaries recognized fixed laws of nature. Every event was attributed directly to deity. Apparently the Greeks saw no incongruity in the tale of Hercules splitting a mountain, nor the Hebrews in Joshua causing the sun and moon to stand still; nor yet, in a flood that submerged all lands.

Although some of the Hebrew writers were shrewd observers of the things about them they used their observation not in constructing a natural philosophy but in impressing upon their hearers their belief in the personal presence of deity. Of an earthquake they said "He looketh on the earth and it trembleth"; or "The mountains quake at Him and the hills melt." Of a volcanic disaster they wrote "Jehovah rained upon Sodom and Gomorrah brimstone and fire from Jehovah out of heaven."

In Christian nations the Mosaic account of creation was for many centuries regarded as history. It was accepted as revelation and therefore as final and indisputable. By some it still is so regarded.

But in time men began to question the foundations of the so-called authoritative statements. The idea that the earth is flat and is the center of the universe was overthrown by Copernicus (1473–1543) when he enunciated his theory. Men in ever-increasing numbers, not satisfied with the brief statement that "God created," are busy trying to determine the agencies employed in creation and the succession of events.

Medieval Opinions

Descartes, in a paper published in 1644, expressed the belief that the earth and planets were originally glowing masses like the sun. Leibnitz (1646–1716) accepted this theory and added much toward developing a conception of a globe that was at one time fluid.

These more advanced ideas did not escape unchallenged. In 1681 Thomas Burnet published a "Sacred Theory of the Earth," which made a strong impression, although it contains a fanciful notion of the earth's structure. The author maintains that up to the time of the Deluge the earth had enjoyed perpetual spring, but that the wickedness of mankind led to a catastrophe in which the sun's rays split open the crust of the earth, which was crushed like an egg, allowing a supposed central abyss of waters to rush out.

William Whiston became still more explicit. In his "New Theory of the Earth" (1696) he demonstrated to his own satisfaction with mathematical exactness that Noah's flood was caused on November 18, 2349 B.C., when the tail of a comet passed over the equator and caused a downpour of rain at the same time that the earth was broken open and the "internal abyss" poured forth water to inundate the land.

Buffon (1707–1788) went so far as to regard the earth and planets as parts of the mass of the sun shaken off by the shock of a comet whereby the "impulse of rotation and of revolution in the same general plane was communicated to them."

It may be of interest to note in this connection that comets have proved to be quite harmless things. The earth has passed through the tail of a comet on several occasions without our knowing anything about it, except for the assurance of the astronomers. On the other hand, it may perhaps be of interest to recall that more than a century after Buffon a theory of the origin of the earth was promulgated that attributes to a passing star an influence similar to that of Buffon's comet.

It is worthy of note still further that Buffon originated the idea of solving the problem of planetary evolution by the laws of mechanics. In his history of the earth he boldly extends the "six days of creation" into six long periods, each having a duration of thousands of years.

Nebular Hypothesis

Buffon was closely followed by the philosopher Kant (1724–1804) who crystallized the most advanced thought of his time and developed many of the ideas grouped together as the familiar nebular hypothesis of our own day. These ideas were adopted in part by the French mathematician Laplace (1749–1827) and expanded by him into the form commonly known as the Laplacian or Nebular Hypothesis.

This hypothesis was in harmony with most of the facts known a century ago, and although Laplace himself put little emphasis on the hypothesis, it seemed to offer a satisfactory explanation of the origin of the solar system, and its author's eminence in other departments of learning gave it an initial impulse which it may not have deserved. However, many modern geologists and astronomers hesitate to discard it now, even though it proves to be out of harmony with some recent discoveries and is not in accord with certain mathematically demonstrated laws. A newer explanation, called the planetesimal theory (or *hypothesis*, for some would assign it to this lower rank), has been developed in its place, which takes cognizance of known laws and seems to harmonize with them. The newer theory has only begun to win its way, and some believe that it will never wholly replace the nebular theory of Laplace.

Chapter XII

HOW WAS THE EARTH MADE?

In referring to the reputed works of Hercules, one of the Latin writers expressed skepticism concerning them, and stated that it is difficult to believe what the poets have said. In like manner some of the current beliefs are questioned. Some modern thinkers have found difficulty in believing what other thinkers have said.

Nebular and Planetesimal Theories

Those who question the foundation of theories make themselves as unpopular in certain quarters as Socrates was with the ancient Greeks when he pointed out to them the absurdity of their beliefs. Recently a speaker who mentioned the fact that serious doubt had been thrown on the nebular theory was accused of being a mental anarchist. "Why," the objector asked, "should things that we have accepted all our life be turned upside down?"

Since the nebular theory was formulated, more than a century ago, great progress has been made in the accumulation of facts relating to the heavenly bodies, and particularly to the earth as one of these bodies. In the light of these facts, this theory has been weighed in the balance and, in the opinion of some, found wanting. The planetesimal theory, founded on modern knowledge, formulated to take its place, is accepted by some and rejected by others.

Behold, now, the working of the conservative mind! We were brought up to believe that the nebular theory presents a true picture of the origin of the earth, and we were quite content in this belief as long as no one said it was wrong. Why isn't it true? Therefore, by implication, of course it is true! How foolish to argue against it! Has it not been law for a hundred years? Volumes have been written about it; universities teach it; text-books are full of it; and even the children of the kindergarten rush home to tell mother that the world was once nothing but steam like that from the kettle. Almost everyone knows, or thinks he knows, that the solar system was once a mass of diffused gas and that on cooling, this mass formed the sun and the planets.

Whatever else may have resulted from the diffusion of gas, many a nebulous tale has resulted. The comparison of Genesis and geology is a favorite theme, especially with some who seem to know little about either.

I recall the stirring eloquence of an orator well known many years ago, as he painted in lurid hues the picture of the cooling earth receiving the torrential downpour of water to form the oceans, and of a thick atmosphere, too murky for the rays of the sun to penetrate. He had learned, perhaps, that the great beds of coal of the Carboniferous period are formed of vegetable matter, and that plants cannot grow without light. Therefore, he called on the thick clouds which shut out the light of the sun to illuminate the earth by electric flashes. How we closed our eyes as the lightnings of that far-off time flashed (in the fertile imagination of the speaker) so constantly that they furnished the light necessary for the growth of forests. And how the thunder (mostly of oratory) roared!

The picture was worked out in great wealth of detail, and really served a good purpose, for it gave the theory a ludicrous aspect and caused some to wonder whether there was really any truth in it.

Such word painting is in the class of an address periodically delivered by an acquaintance of mine who is fond of preaching in support of the story of Jonah and his accommodating whale. He reaches a grand climax with the statement that an all-powerful Being would be able, if necessary, to "prepare for Jonah's accommodation a whale with up-to-date apartments including steam heat and electric light."

Fantastic Interpretations

Unfortunately, such statements sometimes reach large audiences, for fancy runs through many editions while fact is searching for a publisher. And sometimes fancy even creeps into science, the acknowledged realm of facts. Too often unsupported assertions carry the weight of conviction where demonstrated law makes little impression. Witness the theories of the origin of the earth!

Recently a well known publication conveyed to nearly half a million readers the unqualified assertion that the earth was once

> a great, fiery ball, so hot that water can not rest tranquilly upon its surface. . . . All of the carbonic acid that is to supply the carbon to form the immense coal fields and to combine with calcium to form the great beds of limestone is in the atmosphere, and all the water of all the modern seas and oceans, lakes and rivers, is held in a great thundercloud that envelops the entire earth.
>
> There is no light except that from the glow of volcanic fires, and from the almost incessant flashes of lightning . . . rain falls actually in rivers. The roar of the thunder and the crashes of volcanic explosions are deafening. As the rivers of rain strike the hot surface of the earth, they are converted again into steam and thrown into the sky.
>
> The weight of the atmosphere under the ocean of steam and cloud and carbonic acid gas is so great that water must be heated red-hot before it will boil.

Such a word picture has a certain uncanny fascination and recalls the tales told by Baron Munchausen. Yet it is a fair deduction from the nebular theory of the origin of the earth.

Years ago such statements might have passed unchallenged, but now scholars qualified to speak with authority say that such extreme conceptions must be abandoned. Few up-to-date geologists would undertake to defend the statements quoted. We should at least be told that they express only possibilities and that many leading scientists treat the subject differently.

A Cherished Belief

The origin of the earth is a fascinating subject. The belief in the nebular theory is cherished by those who grew up under it, and some of these show a tendency to regard modern thinkers who reject it as agitators trying to overturn an established order of thought.

According to this theory the original nebula, consisting of gas, extended from the sun as a center outward beyond the orbits of the planets. This nebula, which had in some way acquired a rotary motion, slowly contracted as it cooled. Its rotation increased correspondingly until the centrifugal force which tended to throw off the outer portions equaled the gravitative force which tended to hold them to the central mass. Then a ring was formed like the rings of Saturn, which in time became a planet. This process was repeated for each planet, each ring being left behind as the central mass continued to shrink into the sun.

As enunciated by the great French scholar Laplace this theory seemed ample and satisfying. Its very boldness and splendor gave it a dignity which seems to have overcome all opposition. It set forth so clearly the march of events in the creation of the world that it swept aside obstacles to its progress. It seemed to be in harmony with the fundamental relations of the solar system as they were understood at the time it was announced. It was in general agreement with the learning of a century ago. Above all, it offered a clear, easily comprehended answer to the question of universal interest, How was the earth made? Few suspected that the answer which the nebular theory gave might be wrong, and, later the theory became so popular that opposition to it was unpleasant to maintain. Even at the present time an attempt to discredit it in certain quarters seems useless. There is hope for a blind man who wants to see, but none for those who have eyes but will not see!

Difficulty of Changing Established Opinion

As long as there was no great number of well-established facts opposing the nebular theory it ran its course without let or hindrance, and many still hold to the opinion that it is good enough to be let alone. Others not so easily satisfied contend that theories, however beautiful, should not obstruct progress. The false must perish and the true survive!

The opposition to any radical change in established belief is well expressed by the following satirical verse by Charlotte Perkins Stetson:[1]

There was once a Neolithic Man,
  An enterprising wight,
Who made his chopping implements
  Unusually bright,
Unusually clever he,
  Unusually brave,
And he drew delightful Mammoths
  On the borders of his cave.

To his Neolithic neighbors,
  Who were startled and surprised,
Said he, "My friends, in course of time,
  We shall be civilized!
We are going to live in cities!
  We are going to fight in wars!
We are going to eat three times a day
  Without the natural cause!

[1] In this our World.

We are going to turn life upside down
  About a thing called gold!
We are going to want the earth, and take
  As much as we can hold!
We are going to wear great piles of stuff
  Outside our proper skins!
We are going to have Diseases!
  And accomplishments!! And Sins!!!"

Then they all rose up in fury
  Against their boastful friend,
For prehistoric patience
  Cometh quickly to an end.
Said one, "This is chimerical!
  Utopian! Absurd!"
Said another, "What a stupid life!
  Too dull, upon my word!"

Cried all, "*Before such things can come,*
  You idiotic child,
You must alter Human Nature!"
  And they all sat back and smiled.
Thought they, "An answer to that last
  It will be hard to find!"
It was a clinching argument
  To the Neolithic Mind!

The nebular theory was a magnificent conception, worthy of the great mind that formulated it. Through its influence on the thoughts of men it accomplished immense results. But beautiful as it is, it may not be correct. The limelight of mathematics, astrophysics, and modern geology has been turned upon it and has discovered facts that it cannot explain. Many of these facts have been pointed out. One illustration may suffice.

Errors in Application

According to the older theory the earth at one time consisted wholly of melted rock like the boiling slag of some immense blast furnace. As the earth cooled a crust was formed and gradually thickened until a stable surface allowed water to remain on it. At first the water was boiling hot, but later in the earth's history the surface became cool enough to permit plants and animals to live on it. The cooling continued, according to this conception, through geologic ages, and in relatively recent time — that is, during the Great Ice Age — the surface of the earth became so cold that glaciers formed over large parts of it.

At this point the prophets take up the refrain and predict dire catastrophes. They point out the terrible consequences of the inexorable law of cooling worlds. Soon the earth will freeze and die. Is not the moon already dead?

The picture seemed plausible enough as long as only one glacial epoch was known. But in course of time the discovery was made that glaciers covered parts of the earth long ages before the Great Ice Age, at times when, according to the nebular theory, the earth was sweltering under a hot, murky atmosphere. (Why *will* scientific men persist in spoiling perfectly good theories by damaging discoveries!) The evidence of still older ice ages was discovered, one so old that its records are found in rocks laid down during one of the first of the geologic periods.

Origin of the Planetesimal Theory

The planetesimal theory was formulated several years ago by Prof. T. C. Chamberlin, of Chicago University. It has been slow in finding its way into nonscientific circles, but it is worthy of consideration. It is fundamentally different from the old theory. The problems are approached from a different point of view. No attempt is made to expand the new theory into a universal law. It seeks to explain our solar system and nothing more.

Unlike the old theory, the new one is based on numerous physical laws which have been discovered in the course of modern research. It may not now be expressed as clearly as was the old theory, for some of the newly discovered laws are not yet widely known outside of scientific circles. Many of the new words and some combinations of words necessary to express the new ideas are unfamiliar. Until one understands what is meant by kinetic view of gases, earth-knots, planetesimals, krenal atmospheres, and vestiges of cosmogonic states, one can scarcely be expected to understand a theory in which these terms are used. However, difficulty in understanding the nomenclature of a theory is no argument against its truth.

A Collision of Worlds

In place of the concept of a solar system evolved or derived from an evenly diffused gas, this system, under the planetesimal theory, is evolved from irregularly scattered matter of various kinds, some of it solid and some gaseous. This material is supposed to have been derived from a heavenly body already in existence, called the ancestral sun, because it contained the material now distributed among the several planets and satellites. Like every theory that deals with the origin of worlds, it starts with matter already in existence. But it contrasts sharply with the nebular theory in assuming that this matter was in a physical state such as we are familiar with.

The ancestral sun, according to the theory, was disrupted or was partly torn to pieces by near collision with another heavenly body that passed near it. As stars move in different directions and at varying velocities, it would seem strange if in past ages no two heavenly bodies had approached near enough together to interfere with each other. The sudden increase in brilliancy of some stars noted by astronomers is supposed to be due to collision. Hence the postulated interference of a star with the ancestral sun is not only possible but reasonable. The star need not actually strike the sun in order to tear it to pieces and scatter the fractured material; in fact, a head-on collision probably would not produce the rotary motion possessed by the solar system.

Under the laws of body-tides, a star passing near the sun — that is, within a few hundred millions of miles — would interfere with the sun's internal equilibrium and cause it to shoot out a part of its substance toward the passing star and another part in the opposite direction, for the same reasons that tides of the ocean are formed on opposite sides of the globe. The attractive force of the passing star, aided by the internal expansive forces of the sun, is supposed to have caused gigantic eruptions similar in character to those taking place on a relatively small scale in the sun at the present time. During times of solar eclipse eruptions are observed through the telescope, in which great masses of matter are shot far out from the surface of the sun. A more familiar illustration is found in volcanoes of the explosive type. But instead of a cubic mile or two of rock blown from a volcano, the matter supposed to have been ejected from the ancestral sun at the time of disruption contained the substance of future worlds and was shot out millions of miles into space. Under the influence of the passing star material thus thrown out from the ancestral sun may have been given a rotary motion around the parent mass, forming a spiral nebula similar to those revealed by the telescope in many parts of the heavens.

A Nebula Formed

In this way, according to the new theory, was produced the diffusion of matter from which our solar system was evolved. Chamberlin states the case thus:

> The term solar nebula is not here used in the inherited sense of a nebula that condensed *into* the sun and its attendants, but as a nebula evoked *from* the sun to form its attendants. As here interpreted the solar nebula was little more than a streaming knotty

pair of arms of nebulous matter shot out from the sun and curved into spiral appendages about it by the joint pull of itself and a passing star.

The larger aggregates or knots may have retained a high temperature, but much of the widely diffused matter must have been cooled to the temperature of interstellar space — that is, to a temperature commonly known as absolute zero.

The derivation of world matter from the ancestral sun by this disruptive process may not tax too greatly the credulity of the reader if he reflects that only 1/745 of the sun's substance was required to form our whole planetary system; and that the substance of the earth is about one three-thousandth of 1 per cent of that of the sun.

It is clear that, with this fundamental departure from the former conception of a nebula, the new story of the development of the solar system must be very different from the old. The task of writing it naturally fell to the lot of the man who had questioned the validity of the nebular theory. It is an unwritten law in science that an accepted theory may not be destroyed until it can be replaced by something better. In harmony with this law the author of the planetesimal theory has shown how the solar system, as it exists, could be built up from cold matter, irregularly scattered in space. That he has succeeded in forming a reasonable explanation is attested by the number of scientific men who look favorably on his conclusions.

A New System

According to the new theory, the "knots" or relatively dense parts of the disrupted matter which was shot out from the sun served as nuclei for gathering the more widely scattered particles and finally grew to be planets and satellites. It is estimated that the earth knot originally may have contained 30 or 40 per cent of the earth's adult mass. Whether it was composed in whole or in part of hot gas or of particles of solid matter held together loosely does not affect the theory. The scattered fragments, large and small, solid and gaseous, ranging in size from infinitesimal particles to great masses, are called planetesimals; hence the name planetesimal theory.

The earth knot, composed of material originally somewhat closely aggregated, gathered into a compact mass under gravitative force, thus forming a young earth, perhaps less than half its present size. At this early stage the growing earth developed a character that greatly affected its later history, for when less than half grown its gravitational force was strong enough to hold an atmosphere. Previous to this time the unprotected infant earth may have been continually bombarded by falling planetesimals, but the material of its outer half thereafter was brought in from surrounding space through an enveloping layer of gas, which acted as a cushion to ease the force of the bombardment.

So great is the importance of an atmosphere on the growth and character of the earth that we may stop for a moment to consider this subject.

Under the kinetic view of gases the molecules are "fidgety midgets," always apparently in a whirl or a quiver, flying to and fro with marvelous velocity, colliding and rebounding with extraordinary frequency. Their rate of movement depends on many circumstances. Light molecules, such as those of hydrogen, are likely to move rapidly; heavy molecules, like those of carbon dioxide, move more slowly. Molecules of a hot gas move more rapidly than those of a cold gas.

Earth Growth

Gases, like other forms of matter, are controlled within certain limits by gravity; hence the molecules of the atmosphere, although in rapid motion, are held close to earth. But there is a limit to this control. If the resistance of the atmosphere could be removed a bullet shot directly upward with a velocity of about seven miles per second would never return to earth. It might be captured by the sun or by some other body of strong attraction; or it might wander through space like a meteorite.

The molecules of the atmospheric gases may be thought of as minute bullets. If a molecule starts on an unobstructed path directly away from the earth, with a velocity of 6.9 miles per second, it will escape. The earth's attraction is not strong enough to hold it. A larger body, such as Jupiter or the sun, can control the swifter molecules of light gases, but a small body like the moon cannot control even the slower molecules of the heavy gases. This may explain why such light gases as hydrogen and helium occur in the sun's atmosphere but not in that of the earth and why such heavier gases as oxygen and nitrogen are held under control by the earth but not by the moon.

Atmosphere and Ocean

Under the planetesimal theory the earth was once too small to hold an atmosphere. In its early life it may have been as cold and barren and spectral as the moon. But as it grew, by gathering up the solid planetesimals near by, it became strong enough in time to gather in and control the gaseous matter. At this critical stage in its history, as already stated, the manner of its growth changed. Planetesimals falling to the earth had to penetrate an atmosphere in the same manner as meteorites now penetrate it. Probably then, as now, the smaller ones were oxidized and reached the earth as meteoric dust.

In the presence of an atmosphere captured water vapor was condensed and the circulation of water was established. The importance of water as an active geologic agent can scarcely be overemphasized. A body like the earth which grew in the presence of freely circulating water would be very different from

Plate XLVIII. Pensacola, Florida, as Seen from the Air.

At the left are streets and city blocks and a river, bridged at two places. At the right is the Gulf, in which there are sand bars, under water. The narrow white strip in the middle of the picture is a sandy beach. Photograph by U. S. Army Air Service.

Plate XLIX, A. Potomac River Near Fort Washington.

View from the air 3000 feet above the water. The irregular dark, rough parts are tree-covered land; the smooth parts are water. The light belts are deep channels, the broad one the deep natural channel used by the river steamers, the narrow one a dredged channel used by small boats. Photograph by Willis T. Lee.

Plate XLIX, B. Sandy Beach and Swamp Land near Atlantic City, New Jersey.

Seen from an altitude of 10,000 feet. Photograph by U. S. Army Air Service.

a body formed of molten rock and essentially completed before water began to accumulate on it. It may be said in passing that the constitution of the earth's crust, as observed, harmonizes with this theory of accumulation of matter in the presence of water.

In brief, the planetesimal theory pictures the earth as growing from a modest beginning chiefly by gathering in cold particles of scattered matter near it. This growth has not yet entirely ceased, for meteorites are still coming to the earth in great numbers. It may never have been molten throughout and may never have been too hot for the existence of organic matter. At first the young earth had no atmosphere and no oceans. It may have been as cold and dry as the moon is at the present time. An atmosphere began to gather when the earth was less than half grown and oceans began to form somewhat later. In the beginning the oceans were small and contained fresh water. Their present salinity is an acquired character; their salt was derived from the rocks. In place of the postulated hot, murky darkness of early ages, the planetesimal theory pictures the atmosphere as dry, cool, and bright.

The new theory explains many things that seemed inexplicable under the old. It is not my purpose here to attempt to apply the theory in detail. Such application would require volumes. But the following examples may illustrate the possibilities of application.

Anomalies Explained

Good, orderly, well-behaved moons like our own revolve about their planets in the same direction that the planets rotate. The discovery that two of the moons of Jupiter and one of Saturn revolve in the opposite direction was puzzling and disconcerting under the old theory. Under the new, this retrograde motion is regarded as normal.

Under the old theory it was difficult to explain the high

development of the oldest known forms of life found fossilized in the rocks. Biology demanded longer periods for development than geology could supply. But under the new theory, conditions suitable for life on the the earth may extend back indefinitely in time. Biology may now have all the time necessary.

Glaciology called for several cold periods, some dating back to a time when the earth was young. The new theory accommodatingly allows as many as are needed, and sets no limit to their antiquity. In brief, the planetesimal theory seems to meet some of the demands of the progressive age in which we live.

Before leaving this subject, it may be frankly admitted that the planetesimal theory has made slow progress toward general acceptance. It has gained many powerful friends, but enemies have arisen against it.

The opposition to this theory may be due to a variety of causes. The theory may have fundamental defects. On this question there seem to be differences of opinion. Some are naturally reluctant to cast aside the cherished belief of a lifetime. "An old dog does not readily learn new tricks."

Many are indifferent. They care little which theory prevails. Apathy is a difficult enemy to combat.

Among those who are without knowledge of the merits and demerits of the opposing theories, the one which is understood with the least effort is the one most likely to gain acceptance. The argument that a thing is true because it is simple is as curious as it is fallacious. The fact that the nebular theory is more easily understood than the planetesimal theory is no argument in its favor.

Unfortunately the planetesimal theory is cumbered with a great number of unusual terms. Those who are unfamiliar with these terms find difficulty in comprehending discussions in which these terms are used. Unhappily, some valuable suggestions perish because millstones of unfortunate expression are attached to them.

Chapter XIII

FACTS, FANCIES, AND NEBULOUS THOUGHTS[1]

Whatever may have been the original condition of the material of the earth, and whether or not it was once in a nebulous state, the early conceptions of its nature certainly were nebulous in the minds of men until little more than a century ago. It seems marvelous how some of the fanciful speculations concerning the earth ever originated. For centuries people believed tales which now seem so obviously impossible that we marvel that they were seriously considered by any one. But wild speculations gradually gave way as facts accumulated. Many of the myths, legends, and folklore tales have been relegated to the realm of fiction.

Forget the past and look forward is a good rule, but it is sometimes worth while to look backward and view the mistakes made in the past, for by so doing we may avoid blunders. A glance backward over the events recorded in the history of earth science may well cause us to approach the subject with humble spirit.

The insistence on sharp discrimination between fact and fancy is relatively modern. The progress of thought from speculation without facts to demonstration by means of facts was slow and painful. The history of it fills many a volume. Only a few of the great number of recorded incidents can be mentioned here, but it seems desirable to recall a sufficient number of them to indicate the long struggle after geologic truth.

During the early centuries of recorded history scholars, espe-

[1] For further information on the early history of geology see "The Founders of Geology," by Sir Archibald Geikie, and "History of Geology and Paleontology," by Karl A. von Zittel, translated by Maria M. Ogilvie-Gordon.

cially among the Greeks, began to observe facts that tended to force modification of the still older traditions. Had that tendency continued, we might now be far in advance of our present intellectual position. But the Dark Ages followed and much was lost.

With the revival of learning, about the fifteenth century, began the accumulation of data which forced the overthrow of many a wild speculation and which is continually forcing the modification of hypotheses at the present time. We no longer depend on the spirits and goblins of the "medicine man" for revelation in explanation of natural phenomena. To the enlightened mind explanations must harmonize with observed fact and with demonstrated law.

As early as 614 B.C. traditions were being subjected to tests, for Xenophanes concluded from the occurrence of sea shells found in the inland hills of Malta that these hills had formerly been submerged. At the time of Herodotus (484–425 B.C.) fancy and fable were giving place to fact in the minds of thoughtful men. The "Father of History" cautiously suggested that the famous gorge of Tempe, which some attributed to Hercules, who was said to have split the mountain, was not formed by the hero but rather that "the mountain had been torn asunder by an earthquake." Modern thinkers have other explanations, but it is interesting to note that more than twenty-three centuries ago some men were explaining natural phenomena in terms that seem surprisingly modern. Herodotus and others noted the occurrence of petrified shells in the Egyptian hills and concluded from them that the sea had once spread over that country.

Empedocles (492–430 B.C.), a Greek philosopher of Sicily, gave to the world the conception that the earth's center was composed of molten material. He formed this opinion by observing the volcanic activities of Mount Etna. Tradition says that he met his death by falling into the crater of that volcano. One account states that he cast himself into the crater in the hope that men finding no trace of him would suppose him translated but that his secret was betrayed by one of his sandals, which was given up by the volcano.

The Greek philosopher Aristotle (384–322 B.C.) had little to say on geologic subjects, but some of the things which he did say seem strangely modern. For example, "The sea now covers tracts that were formerly dry land, and dry land will one day reappear where we now find sea. We must look on these mutations as following each other in a certain order and with a certain periodicity."

Progress of Greeks, Romans, and Arabs

Theophrastus (368–284 B.C.), a pupil of Aristotle, wrote a special work on fossils. This work is lost, but Pliny refers to it. The idea that sea and land had changed places persisted to the time of Strabo (66? B.C.–24? A.D.), who wrote "Everyone will admit that at many periods a great portion of the mainland has been covered and again left bare by the sea." But in spite of this opinion he seems to be puzzled over the occurrence of fossils. When standing by the pyramids of Egypt he noticed that the blocks of stone that had been brought from the quarries contained pieces which in shape and size resembled lentils. He was told that these were remnants of the food of the workmen turned to stone. He rejected this explanation as improbable but did not suggest a likely origin for them. It is now known that these lentil-like bodies are fossil shells called nummulites. They are so numerous that the rock containing them is called the Nummulitic limestone.

Some of the Romans adopted in part the Greek conceptions and made considerable additions from observed facts. Suetonius relates that the Emperor Augustus decorated his villa at Capri with huge fossil bones, which at that time were supposed to be the remains of a giant race. Pliny (23–79 A.D.), who made large contributions to human knowledge, will always be remembered as the first martyr to natural science, for he lost his life in an endeavor to fathom the secrets of the great eruption of Vesuvius at the time Pompeii and Herculaneum were destroyed.

But although considerable progress was made by the Greek and Roman writers toward conceiving an orderly sequence of terrestrial events, not one of them conceived the idea that fossils could be used as witnesses of such events. This great step toward a science of the earth was reserved for more modern thinkers.

But although a few of the ancients had clear vision, speculation without observation was more general than the accumulation of facts. Fanciful explanations, springing apparently from some fertile imagination without recourse to observed facts, were accepted and reiterated for centuries. Even the very slight advance that had been made by the classical writers toward developing a science of the earth was lost after the barbarians overthrew the power of Rome. Progress in this, as in many other branches of learning, was arrested for centuries. Thereafter, through long, barren ages, narrow, cloistered scholasticism prevailed.

Curious Explanation of Fossils

During the centuries of the Dark Ages little advance was made in geologic science. The Arabs did something toward intellectual progress, but their activities were not directed to geologic research. Avicenna (980–1037 A.D.), an Arabian commentator of Aristotle, followed that philosopher in advocating the theory of spontaneous generation,[1] and outdid his master in picturesque explanation when he suggested that fossils had been

[1] Spontaneous generation remained a burning question until it was overthrown by the experiments of Pasteur (1822–1895), the father of the science of bacteriology.

"brought forth in the bowels of the earth by virtue of that creative force of nature which had continually striven to produce the organic out of the inorganic" and that "fossils were unsuccessful attempts of nature, the form having been produced but no animal life bestowed."

Many an echo of this idea was heard centuries later, when theologians became alarmed about fossils, which they undertook to explain as "unsuccessful attempts of the Creator, or forms never endowed with life"; "models of His works rejected by the Great Artificer"; "outlines of future creations"; "objects placed in the strata to bring to naught human curiosity."

Avicenna was in some respects far ahead of his time. He accounts for mountains in two ways that seem surprisingly modern. He asserts that they may arise "either from uplifting of the ground, such as takes place in earthquakes, or from the effects of running water and wind in hollowing out valleys." Although strongly influenced by the older philosophy, which was based largely on speculation, he was a forerunner of those who base their philosophy on things that they observe. He was separated in time from the old Greek philosophy by nearly a thousand years and from the new philosophy of the present time by a period nearly as long.

Dark Ages and Backward Steps

During the long intellectual night that followed the fall of the Roman Empire the slight advance made by the ancient philosophers toward a rational interpretation of natural phenomena was almost forgotten. Learning was confined chiefly to the monasteries and directed mainly to such subjects as could be pursued within the shelter of their walls. This naturally excluded the science of the earth, which requires study in the open, wide observation, and the collection of great volumes of exact information.

A famous geologist emphasized the necessity for study in the open when he said that three things are absolutely necessary in the study of geology. The first is travel; the second is *travel;* and the third is TRAVEL.

An especially unfortunate decline took place during the Dark Ages — a slip backward toward the primitive age, when little distinction was made between legend, religion, and fact. When parts of the ancient Hebrew writings were collected and combined as The Scriptures, the legendary accounts of Creation were included and were generally accepted as divine revelation.

On this subject, Von Zittel says: "The Mosaic account of Creation was incorporated in the Bible of the Christian Church and unfortunately became invested with a scientific value by the Church. This retarded the development of geology for many centuries, inasmuch as theologians regarded the Mosaic account as an essential dogma of the Christian Church and sought to suppress any investigations and writings of scientific interest which did not harmonize with it."

There is a temptation to censure those who tried to suppress what they believed to be erroneous, and to smile at the gullibility of those who knew no better than to mistake "authoritative" assertions for demonstrated facts. Perhaps, however, our judgment both of the honest dogmatist and of his unsuspecting dupe will be mellowed if we reflect that some of the common beliefs of our day rest on assertions rather than on demonstrations.

Truth and Martyrdom

In the mental darkness of the long intellectual night men lost sight of the contributions made by the ancients. Even so great a catastrophe as that which overwhelmed Pompeii was forgotten. Facts that had been part of common knowledge centuries before must be discovered again. The rediscovery seems to have begun with the revival of learning in the fifteenth century, but under what different conditions from those of the days of Greece and Rome! Ecclesiastical habits of thought had now gained ascendancy over the minds of men, and mistaken zealots sought to suppress, by force if necessary, opinions that ran counter to their own doctrines. But some sturdy characters defied authority, spoke or wrote what they believed, and suffered the consequences.

Some utterances of truth cost the speaker's life. In the year 1553 Michael Servetus was condemned for heresy and burned at the stake. Servetus had done much toward the advancement of science. One service was the preparation of an edition of Ptolemy's Geography, in which Judea was spoken of not as "a land flowing with milk and honey" but, in strict accordance with the truth, as in the main meager, barren, and inhospitable. At his trial John Calvin used this quotation against him with telling effect and argued that it "necessarily inculpated Moses, and grievously outraged the Holy Ghost."

Giordano Bruno, a natural philosopher of considerable insight, who followed Copernicus in teaching that the earth moved about the sun, and who denied that there had ever been a universal Deluge, was long hunted from land to land and, after being imprisoned for six years, was finally burned for heresy at Rome in 1600. Bruno's belated reward for standing faithfully for the truth came nearly 300 years later, when his statue was erected on the spot where he was martyred. A reprint of his ideas appeared about the same time (Boll. Soc. Natur. Napoli, 1895). He described the earth as a spherical body, on whose surface the depths of the ocean were greater than the heights of the mountains. His statement is confirmed by the discovery of an ocean depth of 32,088 feet about 40 miles north of the island of Mindanao, one of the Philippine Islands, and the determination that the highest point of land, Mount Everest, reaches an altitude of 30,292 feet. In his writings is found the statement, now familiar to every school boy, that mountains are no higher in proportion to the size of the earth than the wrinkles on the skin of a dried apple.

In sharp contrast with such bold characters as Bruno were politic thinkers who veiled their ideas in various ways or suppressed their writings during their lifetime; but many threw reason to the winds and wrote volumes of arrant nonsense, which were published seemingly from no better motive than that they catered to the opinions of those who were in places of power.

A striking illustration of the fear inspired by ecclesiastical authority is found in the manner in which De Maillet recorded his convictions. He wrote in 1715 and 1716, but his writings were not put in type until 1735 and were not distributed until 1748, three years after his death. Because of their heterodoxy he would not allow them to appear in print during his lifetime. Furthermore, the unorthodox ideas presented are by him attributed to an Indian philosopher, whom he called Telliamed — his own name spelled backward.

On the other hand, it may be comforting to some but annoying to others to know that the Middle Ages had no monopoly on intolerance, and that a similar spirit prevails at the present time in some places, where men are brought to trial for teaching what they regard as true.

Bruno was an enthusiastic supporter of the natural philosophy advocated by Copernicus, and during his travels through Europe he became disgusted with the attitude of scholars of his time. It is said that an Oxford statute then (in 1583) provided that masters and bachelors who did not follow Aristotle were liable to a fine of five shillings for each point of divergence.

Those who are inclined to smile derisively at this statute may do well to reflect that one commonwealth of the highly enlightened United States of America has a similar law under which a teacher was found guilty and fined for a similar offense in the year 1925.

Science and Dogma

The struggle between scientific and ecclesiastic thought, which was so bitter for centuries, centered in the origin and development of life. It began with a conflict over the nature of fossils. The explanation of the ancient Greek and Roman writers, who had reached the conclusion that fossils were the remains of plants and animals, was accepted by only a few who would not deny the evidence of their own senses and who were bold enough to follow logically the course shown by observed facts.

Leonardo da Vinci (1452–1519) had seen many fossil shells while constructing canals in northern Italy. He ridiculed the belief of his contemporaries that the shells originated "under the influence of the stars" and correctly interpreted them as due to submergence of the land beneath sea level. Some other men of his time held similar views, although these views were much tainted with the idea of a sudden flood.

Georg Bauer (Agricola) (1494–1555), the "father of mineralogy," regarded some fossils as of mineral origin and others as originating from living beings. Mercati (1574) described and figured fossil shells that had been gathered into the Vatican by Pope Sixtus V, but denied their organic nature. He concluded that they were "stones that had assumed their present shapes under the influence of celestial bodies."

Although a few were trying to find a satisfactory explanation of fossils, men were not lacking to deny that fossils had anything to do with life. Falloppio (1557), when he saw the petrified bones of elephants, the teeth of sharks, shells and other easily recognized fossils, refused to admit that they were anything but earthy concretions, because he deemed that a simpler solution of the problem than to suppose that the waters of the Deluge could have reached as far as Italy.

Here we find a curious conflict between ecclesiastical thought and the philosophy of Aristotle, who had written against a universal flood. Martin Lister (1638–1711), a learned Englishman, "combatted the idea that the fossils could have proceeded from animals" (see Philos. Trans. Roy. Soc. London, 1671), although he pointed out that different rocks were characterized by special kinds of fossils and compared these with living forms.

Fossils and the Deluge

About the same time Steno (1631–1687) suggested that certain petrified bones of an elephant were relics of the African elephants brought into Italy by Hannibal. Although a skilled anatomist he hesitated at first to admit that certain fossils were really shark's teeth, but later in life he gave to the world the important geologic principle that stratified rocks are formed from sediments deposited layer on layer, that the fossils they contain result from plants and animals buried in the sediments at the time they were laid down, and that from the strata a succession of geologic events may be determined. He even presented a geologic history of Tuscany. But Steno was also a theologian and felt the necessity of limiting geologic time to 6000 years. He argues that some of the fossils "must be as old as the general Deluge."

On every hand, men were not lacking who honestly and piously tried to reconcile the occurrence of fossils with their theological doctrines. Inasmuch as the account of the Deluge contained in the Mosaic writings was accepted as history, it was appealed to in explanation of the remains of marine animals found in rocks high in the mountains. The Deluge during which "all the high hills that were under the whole heaven were covered" seemed to some a satisfactory explanation, and many of the most ludicrous incidents in the history of geologic science cluster about the endeavor to make observed facts fit this belief in a universal flood.

Robert Hooke (1635–1703), a brilliant English scholar, first suggested the use of fossils in revealing the history of the earth. The nature of these fossils was hardly established before those who believed in the Flood claimed them as "vestiges from the earlier creation interred in the earth during the great Deluge." This idea was widely taught, among others by Schuechzer, a professor at Zurich, who found what he supposed to be "the skeleton of one of these nefarious men whose sins brought upon the world the dire misfortune of the Deluge." Cuvier later determined that this skeleton represents a gigantic salamander and named it *Andreas Schuechzeri* in honor of its finder. The bones are now in Teyler Museum, in Haarlem.

Among the works of Schuechzer is a small volume published in 1708, which is noted for its quaint humor. The fossil fishes are reported as assembled in council to protest against their treatment by the descendants of the wicked men that brought on the Flood, by which these very fishes had been entombed. They discourse of "the irrefragable witness of the universal Deluge, which, by the care of Providence, their dumb race places before unbelievers for the conviction of the most daring atheists." Specimens of their fossil brethren are appealed to — pike, trout, eel, perch, shark — and their well-preserved minute structure of teeth, bones, scales, and fins pointed to as a triumphant demonstration that such perfect anatomical details could be fabricated by no inorganic process within the rocks, as had been maliciously affirmed.

The discovery of shells on the Alps was hailed as confirming the reality of the Deluge which covered all the high hills. The difficulty of washing them up the mountain side seems not to have appeared serious. To those whose credulity could encompass such a flood, a little matter of pebbles washed uphill was of small consequence.

In this connection it may comfort some to know that the ecclesiastical writers were not the only ones to advance ludicrous explanations. Voltaire (1694–1778) suggested (was it in earnest or in jest?) that the shells found on the Alps were the discarded remains of bivalves carried there as food by the pilgrims on their way to the Holy Land.

Figured Stones

It is surprising how persistently thoughtful men clung to the idea that the fossils or "figured stones" originated in ways that now seem so absurd. On this point Geikie remarks: "It is almost incredible how long some of these ignorant beliefs lasted and what an amount of argument and patience had to be expended in killing them. I have been told that even within the last century a learned divine of the University of Oxford used to maintain an opinion that the fossils in the rocks had been purposely placed there by the devil in order to deceive, mislead, and perplex mankind."

According to Von Zittel this school of thought, which had flourished for more than two centuries, was brought to an end by the pranks of school boys. He says:

"A semi-tragic, semi-comic event brought this literature to a close. Johannes Bartholomew Beringer, a professor in the University of Würzburg, published in 1726 a paleontological work entitled 'Lithographia Würzeburgensis.' In it a number of true fossils were illustrated, belonging to the Muschelkalk or middle Triassic of North Bavaria and beside these were more or less remarkable forms, even sun, moon, stars, and Hebraic letters, said to be fossils, and described and illustrated as such by the professor. As a matter of fact the students, who no longer believed in the Greek myth of self-generation in the rocks, had placed artificially-concocted forms in the earth and during excursions had inveigled the credulous professor to those particular spots and discovered them! But when at last Beringer's own name was found, apparently in fossil form, in the rocks the mystery was revealed to the unfortunate professor. He tried to buy up and destroy his published work, but in 1767 a new edition of the work was published, and the book is preserved as a curiosity. Many of the false fossils (Lügensteine) may be seen in the mineral collections at Bamberg, and there are also specimens in the university collection at Würzburg, Munich, and other places."

Although scientific men ceased to talk about "figured stones" and no longer believed that the clay images on which the boys had placed the name "Jehovah" in Hebrew characters had been autographed by deity, the idea seems to have lived in the popular mind. In a poem by the English poet Cowper (1731–1800) may be read the lines:

> Some drill and bore
> The solid earth, and from its strata there
> Extract a register, by which we learn
> That he who made it and revealed its date
> To Moses was mistaken in its age.

The passing of the belief in the Deluge was slow and its death struggles are too painful to be ludicrous. The mental contortions of its adherents, who piously tried to defend it, but whose reason forced them to abandon it, seem almost pathetic. Even as late as the early part of the eighteenth century men recognized as intellectual leaders of their time were busy arguing about Noah's flood and devising such unnatural and even miraculous explanations of fossils as has been cited.

The Swiss naturalist, Bertrand, suggested that the fossil plants and animals had been placed in the rocks "directly by the Creator, with the design of displaying thereby the Harmony of His work and the agreement of the productions of the sea with those of the land." And Edward Lhuyd (1660–1709), who seems to have been one of the strong thinkers of his time, described a thousand species of British fossils and states that the shells are partly due "to fish spawn received into the chinks of the earth in the water of the Deluge." But in his correspondence he brought forward a number of shrewd arguments against ascribing to Noah's flood the fossil shells and plants "which have so much excited our admiration and indeed baffled our reasoning."

Persistence of Beliefs

Although the Deluge is no longer a live topic in geology, the Mosaic narrative of the flood is still accepted as authentic history by great numbers of people. Just as the Tortoise-theory of the earth persists among the Hindoos and the hero-myths among the American Indians, the belief in the Deluge will probably endure in some quarters for centuries to come.

The undying character of the belief in the Deluge was vividly brought to me a few years ago while I was examining coal deposits in western Colorado. A man who accepted the account of the flood as history was living on the side of Grand Mesa, near the outcrop of one of the beds of coal. He had noticed that the coal crops out in many places at the same altitude. In a published pamphlet he expresses the belief that trees uprooted by Noah's flood had floated to the side of the mesa as the waters subsided and had been forced by the beating waves into the hillside along the water line and there turned to coal.

The publication of fantastic speculations is not confined to those living far from centers of culture. Even as late as 1885 a volume was published in Boston in which the author, a college president, spreads arguments over nearly 500 printed pages in support of his idea that the Garden of Eden was situated at the north pole.

Some would gladly regard this work as satire, but in the preface the author asserts that the book "is a thoroughly serious and sincere attempt to solve a fascinating problem." The conclusion, that the "treatise opened with a pathetic picture — it must close with another," is true. The treatise seems pathetic in quite a different sense than that intended. The author says that the polar region is "Eden no longer. Even could some new Columbus penetrate to the secret center of this Wonderland of the Ages he could but hurriedly kneel amid a frozen desolation and dumb with nameless awe let fall a few hot tears above the buried and desolated hearthstone of Humanity's earliest and loveliest home." The author had no means of knowing that a man would one day reach the north pole. In Peary's account of his experience he makes no mention of hot tears, but states that on sounding the ocean he failed to reach bottom at a depth of 9,000 feet. Needless to say, no "hearthstone" was found.

Stumbling Blocks and Stepping Stones

It may be questioned whether so many mistaken conceptions and wornout opinions should be recalled. The earlier ones at least should not be held up to ridicule. They were stepping stones by which we rose to higher things. For the later ones there is less excuse. They are stumbling blocks rather than stepping stones.

In my opinion a review of the long struggle for the truth, the mental groping in the twilight of learning, has two important applications at the present time. Many a modern thinker honestly believes that his conclusions are correct and final. Thousands of his predecessors, at whose conclusions we smile, believed with equal honesty that their conclusions were final. The man who is wise will accept the lessons of history and will sharply scrutinize his own conclusions. He will be his own most ruthless critic. Furthermore, he will state his conclusions cautiously, knowing that they will be tested in the future and will be accepted only in so far as they harmonize with facts.

The second application is one of encouragement for the too-timid thinker. Too often modesty is misinterpreted as weakness, and ideas potentially great are killed by so-called authority.

Inspection of the historic records show that often a new idea has a hard struggle for existence. But if the idea is good, opposition to it may die in time.

The Theory of Copernicus

At the risk of repetition I refer again to the story of Copernicus, which illustrates this point in a striking manner.

After years of thought this Polish philosopher concluded that a belief which was almost universal in his time was incorrect — that the earth was not the center of the universe. Instead, he conceived the idea which is now common, that the sun is the center of our system and that the earth moves about it. Fortunately for his peace of mind his ideas were not published until the day of his death. The volume containing this revolutionary conception was placed in his hands on his deathbed.

But when his teachings became known, a storm of protest broke. They were branded as "unscriptural" and were "forbidden." Martin Luther stigmatized Copernicus as "an upstart and a fool"; in 1616 Galileo was admonished not to teach the theory of Copernicus, and "all books which affirm the motion of the earth" were forbidden. Even to the end of the seventeenth century his theory was held to be "unsafe science," and university professors were forced to take oath not to hold the Copernican theory as to the movements of the heavenly bodies. Still later, it is said that certain schools advertised that children would be taught that "the earth is round or flat, as parents may desire."

Let not the modest thinker be discouraged because "wise" men smile at his presumption and refuse to listen. Large things grow from small beginnings. No great conception springs into being like Pallas Athena from the head of Zeus, fully grown. I can perhaps best illustrate this fact by an actual example.

In 1785 James Hutton read before the Royal Society of Edinburgh a short paper on a "Theory of the Earth." European thought regarding things which later were grouped under the head of "Geology" was then dominated by Werner. Hutton's modest essay, later recognized as a turning point in the history of geologic science, attracted little attention at first and denunciation later, but, although he made little stir in the world during his lifetime, Hutton is recognized today as one of the founders of modern geology.

The Dawn

The advance in natural science, so painfully slow at first, gradually gained impetus. A little more than a century ago enough knowledge concerning the earth had been gathered to form a science of geology. Bruno's conception of the spherical shape of the earth; Steno's determination of the nature of stratified rocks; Arduino's arrangement of the sedimentary rocks into Primary, Secondary, Tertiary, and Volcanic; and Buffon's subdivision of the history of the earth into long periods were followed in the later part of the eighteenth century by such great strides toward enlightenment that the eighteenth century may appropriately be termed the period of the dawn in geology. Many men took part in the awakening. A recital of the complete story would be too long for present purposes, but mention of some of its main features may be of general interest.

One of the most important features was the change in method of thought from speculation without facts to reasoning from facts. The reliance on revelation, which had been strong in the minds of men, had begun to weaken. Advance toward orderly arrangement of facts was slow at first, but progress has been steady.

Belief Versus Fact

In the progress toward the belief in physical law, an important step was taken by Desmarest (1725–1815), who, unlike his predecessors, tried to argue entirely from evident facts and allowed himself no theoretical speculation. This method, so common now that we take it for granted, attracted the attention of his intellectual contemporaries and gained for him admittance into influential circles. But unfortunately his revolutionary attitude did not find favor in all places.

Werner (1749–1817), who is often called the founder of modern geology, exhibited a curious admixture of characteristics. He was an enthusiastic collector of facts, a strong teacher, but a dogmatic theorist, who saw only those facts which seemed to confirm his speculations. Before he had ever been out of Saxony he taught that rock formations were universal and that they could be recognized by the same characteristics the world over. He assumed the former existence of a universal ocean which overtopped all mountains, and he even taught that basalt was of sedimentary origin. The necessity of having land somewhere from which to derive the sediments for the formations seems not to have interfered with his complacency. Perhaps he argued as one of his followers did, "when you meet with an insuperable difficulty look it steadfastly in the face — and pass on." He and his followers boasted that they accepted only facts and discarded all theory, yet at the same time they argued in support of a theory of the earth that was almost as fantastic as the flood-theory of their predecessors.

But while Werner was establishing his "authority," which was recognized so widely over Europe, James Hutton (1726–1797) was working quietly in Scotland, as already noted, toward conclusions that are now generally accepted as well founded. Hutton, like Desmarest, tried to base every conclusion on observed fact, and, as the title of one of his papers expresses it, to progress "from sense to science." His "Theory of the Earth," published in preliminary form in 1785, and in its finished form ten years later, was based chiefly on observation. It is regarded as marking one of the great advances toward a well-ordered science of the earth.

One of Hutton's contributions to science was his habit of interpreting the events of the past as the results of processes that we may observe at present, and much of the progress made in the science of geology must be ascribed to him. Charles Lyell (1797–1875), who was born in the year when Hutton died, carried this method still farther and assumed that geologic agencies had never differed greatly from those now in operation.

The study of stratified rocks has always been so closely associated with the study of the fossils they contain that even so brief an account as this seems to demand reference to two conflicting lines of thought. The nature and significance of fossils were naturally determined by anatomists. Two among these stand out prominently. Lamarck (1744–1829) did much to advance the study of invertebrate fossils, and Cuvier did much to advance the study of vertebrates. In fact, Cuvier is regarded as the founder of mammalian paleontology.

These men were on opposing sides of a question which caused long and bitter controversy. Lamarck was an evolutionist; he argued for the gradual development of one form of life or species from another form. Cuvier believed in what came to be called "cataclysms." His ideas were set forth in a treatise entitled "A Discourse on the Revolutions of the Surface of the Globe." In it he advanced the opinion that the earth had experienced many sudden and widespread disasters, by which the land was overwhelmed by the sea. This idea was supported by the occurrence of abrupt changes in kinds of rocks — changes known to geologists as unconformities — and equally abrupt changes in kinds of fossils, as if the animals living at the time one stratum was formed had all been destroyed suddenly and a new group, represented by fossils found in a higher stratum, had been substituted for them.

Strata and Fossils

This abrupt change in the nature of the fossils was seized upon by those who believed that each plant and each animal was created in the form that it now possesses, and the cataclysms were regarded as marking periods of sudden destruction followed by the special creation of new forms of life. This question was argued long and bitterly, but the idea of gradual development of one form of life from an older form has finally prevailed, and we now know that the unconformities which impressed Cuvier denote long periods that were unrecorded in the rocks rather than cataclysms, and that during these long periods the animals and plants had changed in form to such an extent that many of them are scarcely recognizable as descendants of the older forms.

Progress and Established Law

The final overthrow of the old system of thought and the triumph of the new in the minds of most students of geology and biology was accomplished in the battle royal which took place over Darwin's theory of the origin of species. Theologians quickly sensed the serious consequences to them of Darwinism and militantly opposed it. Luther had long ago spoken their mind when he said "I hold that the animals took their being at once upon the word of God." The controversy was long and acrimonious. But the days of the Inquisition were past and scientific men no longer suffered persecution for their beliefs. They calmly persisted in gathering facts. While the theologians were "throwing Darwin to the dogs" Professor Marsh was busy discovering and exhibiting fossil birds with teeth, which are connecting links between reptiles and modern birds, and arranging his exhibit on the evolution of the horse, which Huxley asserted was absolute proof of evolution.

The orderly sequence of forms showing progressive change

through the geologic ages is expressed as evolution and has come to be widely accepted in intellectual circles as a demonstrated law of nature. Nevertheless some still reject this law. Even in this year of intellectual insight, 1926, a text book is in use in some schools which denies not only evolution but many of the established principles of geology. This curious text seems to illustrate what evolutionists call reversion to type.

I recall also that members of a small sect still argue that the earth is flat and that some of the savage tribes of western America still believe in their wolf-god.

This state of affairs is amusing to some people and amazing to others. What should be done about it? As theological thought is largely responsible for harboring beliefs that are scientifically untenable, it may not be out of place to answer this question as a similar question was answered by a wise man long ago when he said "Lest, while ye gather up the tares, ye root up also the wheat with them, let both grow together until the harvest."

Reversions to ancient beliefs have not of late been serious. One of the last great efforts to stem the tide of evolution was made by William E. Gladstone. But neither his great name nor the force of his pen availed against the facts. Huxley had no difficulty in pointing out his errors on the physical side and Professor Driver showed that he was in error on the spiritual side. Since that time few serious efforts have been made in support of supposed revelation as opposed to demonstrated physical law, and the attitude assumed by Arthur Stanley, Dean of Westminster, has been widely adopted. In an address on the death of the English geologist Charles Lyell, the Dean frankly admitted that there is no agreement between ancient tradition and modern thought and that Hebrew Scripture should not be distorted to speak the language of science.

INDEX

MAN AND HIS WORLD

Northwestern University Essays in Contemporary Thought

Edited by

BAKER BROWNELL

I.—A Preface to the Universe.—Baker Brownell—T. V. Smith—Clarence Darrow—Edwin E. Slosson—W. Lee Lewis.

II.—The World Mechanism.—W. D. MacMillan—H. W. Shimer—Irving S. Cutter—W. G. Waterman—Austin S. Clark.

III.—Mind and Behavior.—C. Judson Herrick—George Humphrey—Joseph Jastrow—Floyd H. Allport—E. A. Burtt.

IV.—Making Mankind.—Clark Wissler—Fay-Cooper Cole—William M. McGovern—Melville J. Herskovits—Ferdinand Schevill.

V.—Society Today.—Edwin E. Slosson—Walter Dill Scott—F. S. Deibler—W. E. Hotchkiss—Stuart Chase.

VI.—Society Tomorrow.—George Soule—Earl Dean Howard—Ralph E. Heilman—A. R. Hatton—W. L. Bailey.

VII.—Problems of Civilization.—Ellsworth Huntington—Whiting Williams—Jean Toomer—Charlotte Perkins Gilman—Thomas D. Eliot.

VIII.—Civilization and Enjoyment.—Alvin Johnson—Susanne LaFollette—Morris Fishbein—Lawrence Martin—Maurice Lesemann.

IX.—Art and the Worth While.—Robert Morss Lovett—Charles Johnston—Llewellyn Jones—Zona Gale—Edith Franklin Wyatt.

X.—Five Arts.—Waldo Frank—Mark Turbyfill—Karleton Hackett—C. J. Bulliet—W. Roger Greeley.

XI.—Religious Life.—E. Sapir—Shailer Mathews—Ernest F. Tittle—Rufus M. Jones—Francis J. McConnell.

XII.—The World Man Lives In.—Bertrand Russell—M. C. Otto—D. T. Howard—Richard T. Ely—Baker Brownell.

PUBLISHED BY D. VAN NOSTRAND COMPANY, INC., NEW YORK